Conversations with Dog

How Canine Help You?

(THE CONVERSATIONS SERIES)

Axel Ienna

Copyright © 2020 Axel Ienna
All rights reserved.
ISBN: 9798644182268

DEDICATION

To all unaware participants who helped forge these conversations; *Baloo, Betty, Blue, Grace, Higgins, Ice, Kiko, Magnum, Poppy. Harry*, and those whose names I will never know: the St Bernard, the German Shepherd, and the dead mop.

CONTENTS

DISCLAIMER — V

1	Introduction	Pg. 01
2	Dog mania	Pg. 05
3	A horse and a big bear	Pg. 11
4	First dialogue with a dog	Pg. 12
5	Hitting the couch with *Sigmund Pug*	Pg. 16
6	My dog, my proxy	Pg. 21
7	Magnum, the gentle donkey	Pg. 22
8	At the dog show	Pg. 26
9	Heart-warming *Ice*	Pg. 42
10	The greyhound in my nightmare	Pg. 52
11	The one whose death I grieved	Pg. 56
12	The one whose death I cheered	Pg. 57
13	Betty and Poppy	Pg. 60
14	Spirit animals and animal spirit	Pg. 67
15	Find the One	Pg. 78

DISCLAIMER

I urge all dog owner friends and acquaintances mentioned in the book to not take offence at anything that may sound disrespectful or offensive towards their canine companion (and de facto, towards themselves, as you might come to agree that pet self-identification is quite a widespread phenomenon).

If anything is to go by as an intention, I aim to be thought provoking, not gratuitously provocative.

1. INTRODUCTION

I am cat guy. A cat fan. In fact, I am so obsessed with cats, I must have been one in a past life or be talking to them in some alternate reality. On the other hand, I've resented dogs for as long as I can remember. A German shepherd throwing me off my pram and toying with me as an infant probably didn't help. Not hard to imagine how a trauma of the sort can obstruct canine affection to develop. Yet, the undeniable mutual enthusiasm between dog lovers and their canine companions amazes me. I can swear that some, even put their adored pet before their own children. Unsubstantiated biased impressions and not verifiable observations of course. Right? When my obsession for the *dog phenomenon* hit full steam, I began to investigate what I could be missing out, despite (or indeed, due to) my aversion towards dogs. Noticing that the word "dog" is "God" spelt in reverse brought to mind *"Conversations with God"* the self-help bestseller. This brain fart for an observation somehow made me wonder; if a non-believer managed to get closer to *God* by talking to an imaginary one, could imaginary conversations with dogs help me overcome my aversion towards them? And just like that, I embarked on a voyage to know dogs, their owners, but also myself on a new level. This isn't to say that I no longer find most dogs unnecessarily loud, yappy, and over cheerful, but I can see now why they are so cherished and popular: they've got something we need desperately in our lives. My quirky canine conversations led to a readership-agnostic *pot-pourri* that neither attempts to please or upset dog lovers, nor to persuade or discourage anyone sitting on the fence.

At the onset, I realised that the first thing I needed to do was to adjust my approach to dog owners. In the past, when openly *confessing* that I *wasn't into dogs* I had occasionally hurt a dog keeper's feelings. Once, I childishly pretexted dog allergy to cut short a chitchat about dogs, I inadvertently ambushed myself in. In other instances, I'd enable the stream of platitudes to flow, faking an interest with manifestly uninformed questions and uneducated assumptions about somebody's dog's tail wagging, grooming, shedding cycles, eating habits, or sleeping posture. Being blunt or feigning an interest never led to a good outcome and I begrudged myself for acting out so idiotically. For this to work, I had to manage my irrational antipathy towards dogs and sound neither disrespectful nor obsequious. Whilst few seem to care whether one is into cats, to admit that *you aren't a dog person* is often sentenced with instant character assassination of the blasphemous infidel. I even became convinced that the borderline pathological relationship nurtured by dog lovers towards their pet biases opinions they form about their fellow humans. They could pivot from finding you perfectly amiable to an antichrist envoy and sinner of heretical proportion, the second they found out that you don't like dogs or worse; that you do like dogs, just not theirs; an. Let me try to bring some perspective to our interactions with pets. You might agree that we can safely assume that -like most people- most dog owners aren't vegetarian. I bring up this inference to illustrate the selective dissociation that conveniently applied to animal consciousness. To a dog owner a cow's consciousness must matter far less than a dog's. Such compartmentalisation is needed for millions of pet owners to concurrently treat their pets like royalty, while feasting on domesticated cattle meat produced by way of a daily genocide decimating two hundred million animals globally (three billion, when extending the statistic to wild-caught animals and fish). That's over twice as many as the ninety million dogs alive in the US in 2019. Let's widen the lens; do vegetarians feel the same way towards carnivores, for eating slaughtered cattle meat, as dog lovers do towards Chinese *gourmets* barbecuing dogs for their Sunday roast? The now globally notorious Asian wet markets exposed by the COVID outbreak, display dozen dog and cat skinned corpses lined up at market stalls along snakes, rats and the now infamous pangolins and skewered bats. Expressed differently: the epitome of man's best friend and most loyal companion for millions of Western households means dinner in millions of others. In the face of such (East-West) contrast, could our emotional attachment to dogs be challenged as disproportionate? Such observation sharpened my grit to get to the bottom of it. I wanted to explore if our obsession for pets could be -at least partly- a compensation proxy, besides its undeniable emotional enrichment. And if it mattered, why so much with cats and even more so with dogs? Why not with ducks or hedgehogs? If cat mania is also a huge deal, the scale is incomparable and cat lovers, by and large, don't seem to foster the sectarian prejudice I found among dog owners. I refer to the proverbial unspoken rule of thumb by which, if you don't like dogs, something must be wrong with you. A bit like people having a gut feeling that men who wear a moustache men can't be trusted, as if they hid something behind the facial broomy curtain.

I must admit that delving into dog mania was paved with awkward moments, but it was also an unexpected insightful catalyst for me to face my own (many) pitfalls which led to confronting my oldest deep-rooted fears. It has also gifted me a lot more that I care to admit at this stage and will be revealed in due course.

Woof that in mind, as one of my imaginary canine lecturers would put it, enjoy this mystical report straight from the horse's mouth.
Well, the dog's...

2. DOG MANIA

North Americans spend the equivalent of Bolivia's annual GDP on their dogs and Moldova's annual GDP on dog healthcare, each year. In 2019, the US alone represented nearly half of a hundred and fifty billion dollars global pet market including fish, small animals, birds, reptiles, cats, dogs, and horses; with about fifty percent of that spent on dogs (Bolivia's GDP) and nine billion on dog healthcare (Moldova's GDP).

Pet ownership has been growing steadily with a penetration rate of sixty eight percent per household versus fifty six percent thirty years ago. I copied herewith a snippet from a report by *Grand View Research* which sums up the US pet frenzy: "*Driving growth at the premium end of the market, consumers are spending more on their pets. An increasing number of Americans consider them to be part of the family. Millennials are choosing dogs and cats over children until they're more settled.*' Meanwhile, in the last two decades, Japan experienced a tidal social revolution of financially independent women walking away from the sacred institution of traditional marriage. Such a (literal) decoupling was met with little resistance from tech-addict single Nippon males treating loneliness with the *Love Plus* virtual dating simulator. They all date *Rinko Kobayakawa,* the same imaginary girlfriend and Japan's first digital celebrity. This societal schism saw legions of urban single women get emotional support in dogs, particularly poodles. Affluent single Japanese women allocate an average twenty thousand dollars a year to breed, groom and enrol their poodles into purpose-built clubs for tiny dogs and their owners to socialise.

These company pets for lonely women adorn tailor-made *Louis Vuitton* dog coats, *Gucci* leads, eat premium gourmet food and attend top-end pet salons twice a month to receive *Academy Awards* nights haircare. In 2019, dog show popularity reached an all-time high, despite the gold medal winner a maximum of only five hundred dollars while spending thousands on dog grooming, long haul flights and hotels to attend international competitions. Dog owners and even sone grooming artists will attend these events on their own dime, to watch their creation worshiped by dog fanatics queuing up to post selfies on social media. Why are dogs so popular? We can safely discard body odour, territorial urinal habits or barking frequency and...frequency. Even if adulating their irresistible looks at dog shows is booming, I believe their ability to express human-like character traits provide better clues as to what make them so appealing. It is often the case that the reason why we like something is rooted in a reactionary causality. I infer that we sometimes *like* something in rection to something we don't like; we're just unaware of it. My contention is that we're drawn towards certain things, not out of freewill but also to cope with some of the world's discomforts (rooted in unconscious fears, be they nurtured or native) and drive our decisions to *like* something. And with fear of abandonment being our number primal fear, what better mate than one whose most celebrated character trait is guaranteed loyalty? A highly probable close second *pet* hate of ours, is fear of being judged, but the *holy grail* of life pursuits has to be that of -no, not happiness but- *unconditional love.*

Modern western wisdom portrays happiness as a lifetime goal which pursuit is even proclaimed as a right, enshrined in the United States constitution. I call bullshit. Such tribute to gullible idealism built on cruel cynicism is just one of the many symptoms defining North American insanity. The pursuit of happiness that was coined and whacked into an *American Dream* sandwich, did become the reality of a micro fraction of the population, at the expense of a disenfranchised majority, left chasing the inaccessible spectre of prosperity and blamed for not trying hard enough when failing to do so. People would be a lot happier if they stopped chasing happiness. Professor Laurie Santos teaches the *science of happiness*; Yale's largest and most popular ever class and the largest ever online course to over a million learners and her *Happiness Lab* podcast is also a world class hit. She offers a more realistic, hedonistic definition of happiness; *having a lot of wellbeing in your life and for your life.* Probably smarter than mindlessly accumulating materialistic milestones, polarising the *haves* from the *have nots* in the process. The delusional notion that privileges enjoyed by the prosperous class boosts the personal ambition of the less fortunate has proven a cynical ploy to trick the general public to accept social class inequalities and avoid social unrest. A concept that goes hand in hand with the grotesque *trickle-down* theory, born out of thin air in the perilous imagination of zealous capitalists. In practice, those sitting at the top either don't spend most of their wealth or spend it offshore, only feeding back a fraction of their cake into the local economy, but aware that those crumbs will be enough to avert upheavals of starved hordes of have-nots coming for their assets and their asses.

If we can't help chasing stuff, I suggest chasing unconditional love as an alternative source to appease our deep-rooted fears of abandonment and of judgement. But where to bolt off after it? Though parents are expected to dispense it to their children, not even the most devoted mum will be immune to disappointment from a child not meeting her expectations which -verbalised or not- form and grow over time. For love between us to work out, it must follow a sustained reciprocity that needs to be nothing short of miraculous to sustain the test of time. Thus, unconditional love can only be fickle and ephemeral and yet, it isn't a nice-to-have feeling to be taken lightly, but rather an extraordinary sensation experienced by most infants and chased subsequently by most adults. As grown-ups, the misleading belief that the sacred mutual unconditional love we felt as children will be resurrected by having our own, contributes to turning us into parents. And it may hold true for some time, but often ends up being marginal in the face of decades of cascading disappointment, mutual resentment and even open warfare that can unleash within families. I believe that's when dogs come in divinely handy and why they become a family home's keystone. Unlike us, dogs *are* capable of giving *sustained* unconditional love, or at the very least, of creating the perfect illusion that they are. And in ways that other domesticated animals don't seem to be capable of. The fabulous proximity felt towards a horse or even the proverbially selfish and ungrateful cat doesn't come close to the seemingly transcendental canine love that seems to truly expects nothing in return. No questions asked, especially since they cannot speak, except to me, as this amazing book is about to reveal.

Their occasional ruining a sofa or inappropriate pooping pale in comparison to the guarantee that they won't ever let you down. Ever. No matter what, they'll be there for you. Besides, the puppies are relatively low maintenance and *uber* grateful for anything you do; every time you feed them is a feast, every time you pet them is the best thing that has ever happened to them and when you get home, it is their favourite thing ever. A romantic partner behaving of the sort would drive most of us mad over time (in no time, even), but we love to see that in dogs, as we do, in young children. I suspect that such spontaneity and total absence of calculation constitutes an expression of vulnerability opening a window through which we feel safe to express our own. Vulnerability doesn't fare well in our fast-changing world where constant multitasking and prodigious resilience has been normalised. Expressing our vulnerability is still broadly perceived as exposing a weakness that is best kept repressed, unless staged within a confined and purpose-built context (such as eulogy, a wedding, a public apology etc...) to justify the emotional hiccup. Thus, whether we are aware of it or not, we spend lavish amounts of energy hiding behind a mask and locked in a shell that we hope, will shield us from the emotional discomfort that a multitude of qualms can cause, such as standing out, being wrong, being right, being dishonest, being too honest, being found out, fear of failure, fear of success, etc...The list feels endless. No wonder we cannot wait to go home and be greeted by a non-judgmental, jovial love ball who has zero agenda, other than to shower us with unbridled affection and gives us back the freedom to behave as nutty as we did when we once felt free.

Thus, I believe dogs may be blessed with a divine attribute that we briefly enjoyed as infants and spend considerable resources chasing as grown-ups in a semi-conscious nostalgia. This would justify enduring the continual tragedy of losing a dog, and the next, who unlike children, leave before their (human adoptive) parents.

In light of that, could Bolivia's GDP be a fair price to pay to ensure the emotional comfort of US dog owners and Moldova's, only loose change to maintain it?

3. A HORSE AND A BIG BEAR

I was traumatised by two dogs early in life; the first, I was a few months old, left unattended by a nanny in my pram when her German shepherd strolling in the vicinity, came for me. He must have been curious to find out what up there in the pram and rammed it down, propelling me out of it, on the floor. I guess that would be the equivalent of a horse barging in your bedroom in the middle of the night to throw you out of bed. I was told that such misfortune happening to an infant could trigger a lifelong hyper vigilance to cope with a lasting phobia (of dogs, in this case).

Few years later, my mum and stepfather had taken my sister and I -aged three this time- to a ski resort in lovely Sestriere, Italy. Once we hit the bottom of the slopes, we stood next to an impossibly adorable spaced-out St Bernard crashed on the snow. I was wrapped in a shabby brown fur coat, looking like a chubby mini-Davy Crockett facing a King Grizzly bear. My stepdad thought it would be fun to sit me on top of the mountainous dog lying at the feet of the mountain. So, he did. The scene was immortalised on two black and white shots of me straddling the giant dog, looking uneasy on the first one and in tears on the second one, while my stepdad's unmistakable grin captured on the shot gave away his self-satisfaction at the improvised photo ops. I was terrified and would refer forever to the still sleepy St Bernard, as the "big bear". Fading into the day of my first dialogue with a dog.

4. FIRST DIALOGUE WITH A DOG

I am in Sweden. His name is Higgins, a Border Collie who I only like because his owner, Anders. is like a brother from another mother to me. Little did I know that Higgins and I were to bond in this country house by the seaside outside Stockholm over a long Easter weekend. Most of the city is closed due to the bank holiday and Anders and I made it a mission to take care of his parents' country house where we spend the day gardening and raking. We shock treat our sore backs at night in the sauna, where his friends join us armed with birch leaves and beer packs. The Swedes take their sauna very seriously and I oblige in the local ritual of stepping out of it for intermittent dips in the freezing sea, before being heading back inside the steaming hut to flog our back with birch whisk and traumatise our bladders with ice cold beer. I love it. After much fun and thermal confusion, we head back to the house, get ready for dinner, organised by Anders' grandma; a fabulous cook who prepared her legendary extra-large *lasagna*. She's delighted to have a guest as appreciative of her food as I am, though even by her Viking standard, she wasn't expecting such an ogre, killing four plates of her divine pasta *gratin*. To be fair, we have worked all day and as a cold-water swimmer, I was the only one who, not only dipped in the three-degree sea but swam in it for just over a minute. With the half dozen beer cans I downed, my appetite is that of *Shrek* who stumbled onto *Oktoberfest*. For once, I had found the perfect excuse to not conceal my compulsive eating habit (read: *disorder*).

We feast and I pass out...

In the morning, I am met with kindness through Higgins' eyes; it is impossible to think for a second that this dog is anything else than a live dispenser of unlimited gentleness. He lacks any of the malice or the ambiguity that can be detected in the human eye. Or perhaps he lacks the malicious, ambiguous human eye that projects its own nature onto others. I suppose that is one of the reasons why I felt instantly comfortable speaking with him. He is neutral and non-judgemental. We're out on the porch after hours of obsessive-compulsive lawn mowing and raking. There's a coping practice of mine, that I like to call *hyper focus,* it sounds more sophisticated and less sociopathic. It consists in *killing time to prevent time from killing me,* whenever I feel anxious, which leaving my cushy urban London surroundings has triggered. I crack opened a beer and after a few swigs I ask Higgins:

- "I am an urban cat, you are a country dog, but don't you get bored sitting here all day?"
- "I don't do boredom. Just happy to be here, with the best owners one could wish for."
- "One *dog* could wish for" I correct. "I give you that. So, you don't mind being owned, I guess."
- "I feel chosen, not owned."
- "Are you saying that you *chose* to be owned?"
- "See me run away?" head shaking sideways, "I can leave any time. I *chose* to be *chosen.*"

I scratch my head, confessing that I barely expected a few "*woofs*" and tail wags.

- "Woof then" he kids with a wink and a tail wag.
- "Oh, we have a sense of humour too, do we?" Another wink follows.
- "I'm no dog fan, but you probably figured this much already." I pursue.

- "It's probably just fear and unfamiliarity. But you probably figured this much already."
- "Check you out, *Mr Smug*... Who knew such a sharp mind lived in such a sleepy head." Third wink...

  "If you don't feel owned and, we can safely assume that you can't be staying for the utterly revolting food, what is it then? Feeling part of the family?"
- "I don't feel part of the family; I am part of it. I was chosen and I chose them too. I am staying because I am where I am supposed to be... But you are right about the food; it suuuuucks," he laments in a doggish howl, his paws now covering his eyes.
- "I knew it! Why the grotty dry stuff that makes breath smell like death??" I rant in support.
- "Well, it's a bunch of things; ease of storage, profit margins, plus the stuff contains all the proteins we need, and they think that it must stink for us to be drawn to it."
- "Does it though?... It doesn't, does it?"
- "No, it doesn't!" Higgins howls in protest.
- "Not just a pretty face huh..." I stutter in a bemused stupor, as the cheeky winks again. "Tell me, *Higgy Giggly*; since I am the only one who can talk to dogs, aren't you frustrated to not let your owners know how smart and how funny you really are?"
- "Oh, they know. Haven't you heard of body language?"
- "Hilarious! And how do you express your *body language*?" I dare him, air quoting my words.
- "You know...like that" he replies, air quoting by flicking his perked ears up and down.
- "Wow! Can anyone else see you air quote?"

- "Let's see; given that this dialog is the figment of your imagination to help you process your aversion to dogs; probably not."

There goes down the rest of my beer, at gulping speed, builder style. He woofs some more:

- "For the record, you might not like dogs much, but neither do I. Deep down, I fear that they might take away what I have got here."
- "I feel the same way about loved ones."
- "I thought you might. Fear is in all of us" concedes Higgins, who effortlessly created a lovely bound between the two us.
- "I'm not prepared to hug you yet but from now on, I'll refer to you as *Huggins*."
-

My first conversation taught me that perhaps, I should pay more attention to substance and less to dog appearances making me feel ill at ease around them. And come to think of it, I could be wiser for putting this epiphany into practice with individuals around me too. I got to open a second beer, as Higgins wandered off to rest his nose in his paws and I went back raking with much to ponder, and the reminiscent improbable images of Higgins "ear quoting" dancing in my mind.

5. HITTING THE COUCH WITH SIGMUND PUG

Blue is a black pug. A *"Darth Vader'* toy lookalike on four legs and in my inexpert view, an attention seeking bully in constant demand of care, petting and food. Blue would eat anything. Not just anything edible; anything chewable. He munches to destroy and finds palpable pleasure in compulsive chewing. Boy, he repulses me... Blue is the only dog I failed to tolerate despite deeply caring for his owner. I failed to get past the relentless panting, the nauseous smell, and faecal delicacies left around the patio to mark his territory. When he was not roaming the backyard, engaged in dog intrigue, Blue was almost constantly exulting in whatever it is that dogs exult in. I had no problem with his panting or happy woofing of a dog discovering hidden treasures, but it took me a while to adjust to the sight of his hips twerking, his tongue relentlessly sticking in and out of his mouth and his pitch-black eyes stare, making him look unpredictable and mad. One day, I caught him during his recovery downtime, flopped onto the floor, looking calmer than usual. I tried to engage into a hypothetical conversation.

- "How *ya* doing, pug?" I casually murmur.
- "Always good when around you guys! I know you are no fan of mine, but I like you anyway."
- "Yuck." I find his magnanimous demeanour even more annoying: "That's nice... I guess. So, you can you tell I feel uneasy around you?"
- "Course I can. It's obvious. And it is not just my funny Darth Vader looks, is it..." the pug deducts, revealing a diabolical sixth sense.
- "No...," I chuckle, "it's also the optics, and if I'm honest, the smell, the panting..." I confess.

- "One cannot please everyone I suppose. Let me ask you; could it be that my panting, smell or even my looks remind you of a forgotten someone who made you feel uneasy?"

I pause in bewilderment, giving some thought to his audacious punt.
- "I suppose it's possible. But how to remember someone I blocked off my mind?" I ask, purposely omitting that, digging deeply buried memories up is precisely what I do for a living as a hypnotherapist.
- "Alright then," he continues; "why don't you close your eyes and try to remember anyway."
- "What? What are you a stage magician?"
- "Go on, play along. Wat have you got to lose?"
- "Be warned, *Puggy Poo*, if this is a ruse to come near and lick my face, I *will* retaliate!" I exclaim, in my best menacing tone.

He keeps quiet and stares until I capitulate and comply. And so, I close my eyes to reconnect with the past, in search of a potential link. To my surprise, after a moment, a light bulb sparks in the meanders of my mind and I hear myself say:
- "In primary school, our music teacher was a chronic chain smoker who struggled to breathe, so much so that you could hear her grunt and gasp for air, when she wouldn't be puffing on a cigarette during recess."
- "Did she smell? Say of smoke?"
- "Fuck yeah, the old bat reeked of smoke, and of the cheap musky perfume she used to cover up the nicotine, and the booze stink. She was an alcoholic, drinking on the job."
- "I see. And did she look ordinary, or a bit out of the ordinary?" *Professor Blue* carries on...

- "Well, the old bat *was* actually blind as a bat, with *Mr Maggoesque* thin eye slits hiding behind large thick black framed glasses...And come to think of it, she had disproportionately short legs...She was short, but short legged, even for a short woman."
- "Well, well, well," he punctures, ignoring my last comment, "is it not a funny coincidence...?"
- "Look *Doctor Puggy*, I'm all for introspection and constructive feedback, but what are you hinting at here? I am at a loss."

Blue just stares quietly, as a therapist in session withholding feedback for the patient to form their own conclusions till I venture a timid hypothesis:

- "I'd be put off by you, because you remind me of a teacher who I used to be repulsed by?"
- "Bingo!" Blue approves, breaking his self-imposed omerta and continues; "do you remember how she made you feel?"

Miffed by mocking tone, I exult:

- "Oh, come on! What are you now, Sigmund Freud? Professor *Pugmund Freud*? Why don't I just lie down on the sofa while you grab a notepad and a pen with those paws? And put a pair of glasses on, to really look the part while you're at it!"
- "You mean the same pair of glasses your teacher wore?" the pug boldly hints, adding before I can feign further indignation: "well, suit yourself. You're probably right, I must be an annoying short-legged mucky pug, adored by the whole neighbourhood, but you."

Realising that I might be the contemptuous one, I de-escalate the tone to co-operate:

- "She wouldn't let me help her climb the stairs or carry her bag... Powerless. I felt powerless."

Needless to say, I had never thought of it that way. I had in fact, never thought of it at all.
- "There we go. Now, therefore," *Darth Pugmund* pursues in a somewhat graver tone, "could it be, that my funny looks and my breathing impairment trigger that old sense of failure in you, which you subconsciously process as disgust, because you are, so far, unable to identify its root cause?"

At that point, I sit back in the armchair, slow down my breathing, stare at the ceiling, to process what sounds like a *tree hiding the forest* comment which I intuit, could lead to some sort of epiphany.
- "You know Blue, it does resonate. I am starting to believe that you could be right."

Still not providing feedback, I just get the piercing Blue "*blue steel*" look (that really, is black in his case) until I eventually venture further.
- "My aversion to dogs would find its origin in individuals they remind me of... which if true, would imply that my infantile dog traumas would only be partially to blame?"
- "If at all," a satisfied Blue nods in agreement, "if at all...What was her name?"
- "What was whose name?" I casually asked thoughtlessly, still processing details of the previous implications.
- "The grotty music teacher I remind you of!" Blue yaps before paw facing to mark his impatience.
- "Oh, her name was......did you just palm face...?

I am served another *paw* face and silent treatment which I read as another sign of despair along an urge to *just answer the bloody question*.
- "Riviere. Her name was Marine Riviere,"
- "Does *Riviere* mean anything in French?"

- "Why? How do you know I speak French?"
- "So, what do *Marine* and river evoke to you?" the freak asks, dismissive of any explanation and performing an insane sideways air ninja paw strikeout!
- "Marine is a type of blue and rivers are...also blue. Sigmund *Pug:* are you telling me that besides looking like Darth Vader, being wiser than Yoda you're also the reincarnation of my former crazy alcoholic music teacher!
- "I'm whatever I trigger in you" replies Blue, who also look a lot like Mr Magoo.

With that, I realised I'd be wise to pay attention to dogs' uncanine -I mean, uncanny- ability to connect the dogs -I mean, the dots- between the familiarity and resemblance that dogs crossing my path could bear with people I knew. It reminded me that dogs often look like their owners, who pick them to their own image. A quick online search for "*dogs that look like their owners*' provided ample evidence of it as well as robust entertainment. I began to wonder if beyond alleviating some of our fears, common personality traits were another binding force uniting dogs and their owners. Blue leaves me with further wisdom to mull over.
- "Next time you find my compulsive eating revolting, ask yourself *who t* reminds you of."
- "Touché," I replied.

The *pugger* -I mean bugger- figured me out alright... No pug intended...I mean *pun* ...

6. MY DOG, MY PROXY

Self-identification runs deep within the human psyche. The conceptualised self ("*I am my job, my hood, my religion, my political views*" etc..) provides an anchorage without which, we just can't function in organised society. Even if *I* identify as a free spirit, *I* only operate a conceptualised self and live by the beliefs that being a free spirit suggest to my mind. Understandably, dogs are no exception -and a great addition- to our conceptualised *self* spectrum. They project a coveted untarnished love, making the "*I am my dog*" self-conceptualisation very appealing to our subconscious search of positive identification reinforcement. Besides, the sheer presence of dogs can help with conflict resolution and communication, which their owners use at will, as a proxy to express their mind and feelings to others. Dogs are the perfect conduit for irritated husbands and wives to indirectly funnel passive aggressive messages to each other. Let's face it: marriage can become a near constant battle that often consist in teaming up to resolve issues that weren't there to begin with had we stayed on our own. Thus, dogs are an unaware force for diplomacy and pro bono marital counsellors, mitigating human contradiction and complexity in the household. They are no ordinary family addition; they not only facilitate communication they also provide a mirror reflecting our own attributes and flaws that can help us evolve if we care to pay enough attention. No wonder, a dog passing plunges an entire family into the same grieving cycle as losing a member of the family.

7. MAGNUM, THE GENTLE DONKEY

Magnum is a Great Dane. A giant dog. Albeit a gentle giant. He stands taller on all fours than most children on their feet and fetches two meters (6'5ft) when stretched. He is more akin to a donkey than a dog, with a big blocky head, characteristic of the Great Dane breed. To me, he was real life Scooby Doo without the goofy looks; just a plain scary monster triggering my childhood trauma.

Much like a donkey, Magnum is very muscular, with a terribly loud and irritating baritone bark, a ferocious appetite and a meter-long bull whip for a tail, that leaves permanent deep tissue scars if it comes wagging anywhere near your skin. Like most dogs, he's triggered by the most subtle noise, and he is the ultimate intruder deterrent: the cable guy's worst nightmare. He had once traumatised a FedEx man, onto whom he was ready to pounce, with a savage growl, teeth uncovered, the pricked ears pressed close backwards on the head. I first saw Magnum, over *FaceTime*. I had arranged to fly over to Philadelphia and spend a few weeks with his owners, dear friends I had not seen in years and moved to Radnor, one of Philly's charming suburbs. A few days before my flight we had arranged to chat online and that was when I saw Magnum, pop in the background. I wasn't aware that they owned a dog, let alone one that resembled a small horse. Realising that I was going to spend weeks trapped with the unthinkable, considering my terror of big dogs, I immediately considered canceling my flight. Regrettably, at the time I was in between homes and part of the plan was to remain rent free while staying in the US, so that wasn't going to be an option. Once I hung up, my mind went straight into fight or flight response mode, denial, panic, making up unrealistic coping strategies. There was no escape; I was going to have to face *this thing* (the only term I could use to refer to Magnum at that point in time). Few days and a long-haul flight from London later, I land in Philly as planned. I arrive at the house where I get to reunite with my friends. After long overdue hugs, I am being given a tour of the three-story house and we are in one of the bedrooms upstairs, by one of those American-sized spacious walk-in closets when Magnum (who was supposed to be kept outside until I settled) barges in unexpectedly to check me out, the new kid in town. I only manage to stay still because I froze, as the small horse reached me, rather majestically it must be said, his hips twerking. He is sniffing and inspecting me. Despite being spaced out by the flight, fear overflows my cool and I can't wait for *the thing* to leave my sight and especially for me to leave his. During my first two weeks, each day spent at the house was a challenge. I'd try various coping tactics to de-escalate the unease around Magnum; obviously avoid him as much as possible and use contextual reasoning with mantras such that *this is America, everything is larger in America* (the house is seven hundred square meters, with three cars in the garage, including a *GMC Yukon,* one of the world's top five biggest *SUVs*'). Other times, I'd visualise him reduced to a *Chihuahua,* but he'd show up to remind me that his head alone, was bigger than a *Chihuahua*. His being constantly gentle helped me cozy up to his presence. A few days in, I began patting his back, albeit out of obligation, as he'd force me into compliance by ramming his hips into mine to present his large donkey derriere for me to pat.

His owner shared she'd never seen him so keen to be patted, which made her happy to see me included so fast in the family by Magnum, while I despaired and feared being cursed and paying for bad karma tied to a past life. By now, I have been lectured by *Professor Blue* on mirror and transfer psychology, so I begin to wonder if Magnum reminded me of someone I knew, but no-one came to mind. I began talking to him when the two of us were left on our own for a short week that felt like a full year. I would feed him in the morning, let him out, back in, clean the mud he'd bring back from outside and pat his derriere whenever it was presented. Thankfully, Magnum was so upset by his owners' absence, he'd take abnormal prolonged naps for most of the day. The unmistakable depressed look on his face gave his mood away, so one morning, I finally took it upon myself to engage in a chat hoping to take him out of his lethargy, if not to cheer him up.

- "I know that you miss them, they'll be back in a few days, sooner than you think."

He looks at me with his weary Scooby Doo eyes and looks down again, defeated.

- "To be fair, you aren't exactly in luck, stuck with me while mum and dad are away…"
- "Better off here at home than in a dog hotel. Went once." he woofs in a doggish lament.
- "I sure agree." I say, with a hint of pride.

Magnum doesn't know, but two weeks earlier, I had been out with his mom touring dog hotels for him to stay while they were away, and found them so ill-adapted that, against my better judgment, I insisted he stayed at the house and committed to look after him. That was how I ended up stuck with him in a strange solitary confinement.

- "You are a dog, so you must sense that I don't feel comfortable around you. Am I right?"
- "Sure. As you say, I'm a dog. Sensing stuff is what we do."
- "So, if you don't mind me asking; what's with the whole derriere patting business?"
- "I love it! And it's good for you to heal your..."
- "Let me guess; fear of dogs?"
- "That's right." he mutters, his heavy eyelids closing.

Boy, that donkey was one depressed donkey... I wonder whether it was the absence of his beloved family or I, that made him look so exasperated. I try to create some sense of camaraderie between us, looking at him in the eyes with empathy. With pricked ears, he watches me for a bit and yawns. The obvious absence of chemistry between us is only challenged by his loving me patting his butt so much. Then it hits me; he must remind me of the *German Shepherd* who rammed me off my pram when I was an infant.... of course! He looks as uninspired as ever, raising an eyebrow before resting his nose in his paws, which I read as a sign of capitulation before our ability to bond.

Weeks went by and although I had got used to Magnum, I left America, unable to understand what a monstruous dog was doing in a home housing two adorable children. My fear-based intolerance and I eventually flew back to London.

8. AT THE DOG SHOW

Back in London, I started watching dog shows on *YouTube* and decided to attend one. One could discover many specimens at once and hopefully mingle with some. And thus, I booked a ticket to attend the London Dulwich dog show, advertised as the *"Pawfect* Family Event". Being single wasn't going to stop me, fully confident in my social skills to bond with strangers. And bonding I did.

On D-day, I walk into the venue; a giant hive buzzing and humming with visitors swarming around stands selling all sorts of products, accessories and edibles which mystify my profane senses. Among what caught my attention were treat launchers, rear gear butt covers, polish nails (tagged *pawlish* nails), puppy umbrellas, custom pup purses, dog overalls (for muddy plays) superhero costumes, Victorian dresses (labelled "unisex' not to hurt the transgender puppies I guess, didn't ask), dozen dog necklaces, leashes and a dining table clip-on pet *high chair* for small dogs as if to purposely ridicule them, though I was assured it was a serious article *to include dogs at the family table*. Touring the commercial stands left me dizzy and struggling to fathom why would anyone purchase some of this stuff, but it did bring the answer as to how the USA spends the equivalent of another country's entire GDP on their dogs; by buying shit neither they, nor their dog, need. I then stumble upon a sign reminding pushing the limits of dog mania one notch further: *Dog Psychologist.* Of course... Nothing says *healthy nation* that one sending their dog to a shrink...Too curious, I stop by, greeted by a staff member enquiring at once about the breed I own.

- "I don't own one myself," I reply earnestly, before lying "but I spent time with a dog who I think could do with mental health support."
- "Does that dog live around here?" the staff member follows up eagerly.
- "Well up north…" I double down on my idiotic lie realising I'm the one who needs a shrink!
- "Well, enjoy the show" the lady cuts off with a fake but decent smile, to get rid of me upon realising I'm of no commercial value to her.
- "Before I go, could you just tell me; how can you tell a dog needs psychological support?"
- "We can't. We just prey on owners' credulity, they'll pay anything" gratifying me this time with a warmer smile, before reassuring me; "just kidding. All our therapists are dog trainers and vets, most specialise in a few breeds only, they know exactly what a healthy behaviour is for each breed."

My puppy rolling eyes seem to prompt her to go on:
- "Behavioural troubles start when dogs are with their masters or with pet peers. Masters have to see the psychiatrist too. It is particular to dog and cat therapy: vets have to take into account the subjective and distorting prism through which masters look at their pets since animals project that back. In first session, the psychiatrist spends five minutes with the dog and fifty with its master."
- "Fascinating!" I exclaim, for once not faking an interest in a dog related matter. The flurry of unwarranted information didn't come as a shocker. By now, I'm aware of the dog-owner mirroring dynamics, and I welcome this intuitive deduction of mine being validated by a professional. Yet, I have a further enquiry.

- "If dogs project how their masters feel they must at the very least be empathic creatures."
- "They are emotional sponges. Dogs can read a room in seconds and some of them are excellent at defusing tense situations."
- "I knew it. When you say some of them, does it mean some are extra sensitive and better at handling human emotions than others?"
- "That's a fair depiction. And, some are just dumb as a rock, to be fair."
- "I knew it too!" I exclaim, feeling avenged, for some obscure reason. "One last question if I may; how many breeds are there out there?"
- "There are two hundred and five certified by the *British Kennel Club*, meaning eligible to attend dog shows and probably another fifty breeds that we know of on top of that."
- "So, if as you said each therapist only focuses on a few breeds that they specialise in, you must employ around… forty therapist or so?" I venture.
- "Wasn't your previous question your last?" she concludes, with a wink but also a stiffer smile, signalling that it is time for me leave her sight.

I've seen enough of the commercial stuff; time to dive in the thick of it, check out the contests, see what the show is all about. Much of it looks like snippets I watched online; a huge green luxury vinyl floored showroom where over groomed dogs on their best behaviour stand straight as an arrow while being inspected by professionals. Other contestants are walked on a lead by their masters to be assessed by specialist jury members, scribbling on their notepads. I spot a small crowd listening to a tour guide lecturing on specificities, similarities, and differences between the dominant breeds parading at the show. I spend the next fifteen minutes spoon-feeding my brain with that providential crash course. The man comments large photos of each breed he holds up so that we know what a terrier looks like and the five categories they fall into (large, medium, small, bull type, and toy terrier; a rat on disproportionately tall legs). He goes on to describe how greyhounds and whippets are remarkably similar but different in size, in that the whippet is a "mini-me" version of the greyhound. Both have long narrow heads that are wider between the ears, their muzzles are long, and their eyes are large and round or oval in shape. We're told that there are around thirty different breeds in the *herding* category with the hyperactive workaholic collie and the brave Australian shepherd being among the most coveted for their resilience. Our speaker concludes by revealing that the most sought-after dog of the herding category is the Chinese Shar-Pei (whose name translates to *sand skin*). That is due to the breed's characteristic harsh coat and the fact that after a tax increase in 1947 in China, Shar-Pei breeding was banned for decades, making it an endangered breed and the world's rarest dog in the 1978 Guinness Book of Records. Before closing his tour, the man urges us to look for Jack Russell terriers performing the obstacle course, a prize I instantly decide not to chase, as I have already inadvertently watched one on YouTube and found it soporific at will. Our small group breaks off, I go about and spot the categories in which dogs participate; *best dressed*, *best groomed*, *best trick*, *waggiest tail*, *cutest pup* (puppies under one and a half years old) and everyone's favourite; *the best six legs*. I wonder how exciting can the *waggiest tail* contest ever get.

I can sense the intensity of the competition grow, the trainers' excitement is palpable as they parade pets before the jury and hordes of curious dog enthusiasts. I can't help wondering how the dogs feel: do they know why they're there, that they're competing against one another? Are some of them *dumb as a rock* as the sexy sharky canine therapist suggested? Is their owners' stress passed onto them as she claims? If so, is that a healthy bonding experience or could it be detrimental to the dog's well-being? Well aware to be in the last place to find an unbiased answer, I keep my metaphysical interrogations to myself, my big mouth shut and go on to enjoy the show, or at least, try. That's when I realise the absence of something I had dreaded and even mentally prepared to face in meditation the evening prior to the event; dog smell. No dog smell...Joy! The intensive grooming and *deaug de toilette* must be sanitising the venue by covering the canine scent beneath, alleluia! I made eye contact with an unusually dressed, ragged hippy middle-aged lady. She handles an awfully hairy dog, lined up to be assessed by jury members. She looks nervous and I think, now that I know that the dog-master dynamic is symbiotic, if I could make her feel more relaxed it might rub off on her dog. The specimen is unknown to me and to my untrained eye it looks like an odd, thick rope sack; a mop on legs. I put on my legendary ice breaking friendly face and venture a candid question asking if she owns the dog and if it has been reviewed.

- "Yes, I do. And not yet. We're waiting," she replies before coughing heavily as chain smokers often do.

- "I am sure he'll do great," I continue in bad faith, referring to the mop, "what's his name?"
- "*Her* name", the owner corrects "she is Grace."

Well, here's one hell of a fucking misnomer, if any! Had I not been attending a dog show, I honestly could not have told whether I was looking at a *moppy* dog, a doggy mop or an actual mop. A *Gremlin* or the name *Chewbacca* come to mind as a more intuitive pick for the odd creature, but....*Grace it is*....of course... However to my judgmental mind this brings further confirmation that, if masters project what they are like onto their dogs, they must also project what they lack, and perhaps, aspire to have. I found out later that *Grace* was a thick corded coat dog of the *Bergamasco* breed, once I Googled *Dogs looking like mops* on my phone, where her breed came up straight away, alongside other fluffier versions of her breed such as the *Puli* and the *Komondor* under a search result entitled *Six dogs that look like a mop*. I wonder if behind the thread curtain covering Grace's derriere, she adorns one of those rear gear buttcovers I had seen earlier at the stands. That is when I notice that I can't even tell her front from her backside! To me, they truly are indistinguishable. And so, I wish her well:
- "*May* she live up to her name, may grace prevail!"

Grace of *Chewbacca*...My obvious lack of tact left the lady perplexed with a visible "*why me*" look across her face. Owning up to my social ineptitude I give the poor woman the best version of a smile as my feet switch to autopilot mode and improvise a *moonwalk* to get me out of her sight (possibly Grace's too, provided that I faced her front side). Out of guilt or obstinacy, instead of backing down, I carry on drifting about to find myself drawn to another dog and my two next victims, looking after it. A Japanese couple welcoming my half-baked interest in their dog with the courtesy typical of the great people of the *land of the Rising Sun*. They turn out to be most charming and I find myself drawn towards *Kiko*, their poodle. It must be said, she does look like a lamppost from afar, but has the cutest looks and moves with an elegance that resembled a dolphin on a catwalk. Her owners explain that they flew her over from Japan two months before, to abide by the British quarantine rule and give her extra time to deal with PTSD. Since they own a house in Kent where they spend the summer after the show, they don't mind. Their civility makes me want to spend more time in their company for the sake of it (Nippon liquor enthusiasts; no pun intended). Since Kiko, has already been inspected and the lady seems keen to wind down, we engage in a chat.

- "English and American juries are different from the ones in Japan," she explains, "they are more into symmetry whereas Japanese grooming is more creative and..." she pauses to pull her smartphone for assisted translation: "*adventurous*," she adds.

She makes me feel comfortable enough to confess my rampant ignorance on the matter:

- "I don't know much about dogs; my first dog show. To me, they all look incredibly well-groomed and well behaved. And the dogs look good too."

To my relief, they burst out laughing at my lame joke. The gentleman even showing an inclusive comment.

- "Dog grooming is like art. The best judge is often a fresh pair of eyes and low expectations. You're as good a judge as anyone."

Even though we just met, their effortless gentleness -albeit cultural- feels uncannily familiar, I'm unable to pinpoint why. The lady hands me a small green tea flavoured bean cake pulled out of an exquisitely designed box, typical of Nippon perfectionism.

- "This cake is delicious. It is light and balanced."
- "Just like Kiko," her owner comments. "Poodles are loyal but also independent, elegant and dignified. They are a noble breed."
- "I understand why they're so popular," I nod, "I heard that Japanese single females are keen on poodles. Do you see that? And is Kiko always groomed with those furry balls around her legs or is it only for the show?"
- You are right, Japanese women have gone poodle cuckoo," she laughs, "and these are called *pom-poms*, she has some on her legs and part of her torso under her head. Originally, poodles are water retrievers; their coats are clipped and shaved to help them float but some hair is left to keep the bottom of their legs warm as well as around their vital organs. That's why they look the way they do."

Each of Kiko's legs is shaved but for the bottom, that is meticulously bubbled in a perfectly groomed white hair ball making them look like a giant one-sided Q-tip or. So far, Kiko and other groomed poodles I spotted remind me of the canine version of a bonsai tree but knowing that they are groomed to serve a purpose, I no longer see Kiko a as victim. Galvanised by her hospitality I thank the owner for sharing her expertise and think, why not use my canine psychic superpower to have a chat with Kiko? So, I ask her couple if I could *speak* to Kiko in private. As soon as the word *speak* came out of my mouth, I begin to panic, which triggers my go-to coping mechanism of acting out stupid which, in this case, spurs my hands into forming the well-known Japanese hand clapped prayer sign of respect, to punctuate my request to speak with Kiko. To my surprise, they accept without blinking, no questions asked, no hand sign, no bowing, they just take their yummy cake box, step aside and go watch dogs being paraded around. The embarrassment and craving their cakes gone, I am now alone with Kiko:

- "I feel like I've known you all my life and I feel comfortable with you, which is quite an achievement given my aversion to dogs."
- "In Japan we're not considered as dogs but as an extension of our owners; personality, heart and soul," replies the goofy poodle, "neither they nor we believe in random selection but rather in deterministic reconnections."

Whaaaaaat the fuck was that? Haven't heard someone say something that thought provoking in a while! I pause to string a response together:

- "This would make Nietzsche proud! I'm starting to believe that there's a true metaphysical dog-owner bond."
- "Believe away" confirms Kiko the lamppost, "and the terms *master* or *owner* that they use to refer to themselves and *companion* to refer to us is fear-based rhetoric to create the illusion of control over us, so that we don't abandon them. Whereas we see them as our *soul* family."
- "You mean your *sole* family?

- "No, *soul*. The family meant for us. The one."

That reminds me of Higgins in Sweden assuring me that dogs and owners picked one another. I also heard the same thing from a family I knew personally, when describing their child's adoption process.

- "Abandonment huh…Do you think the same is true between humans?" I ask Kiko, "Do you think we somehow pick our parents, as we do our friends?"

She stares at me, as if to demand my full attention:

- "Any dynamic between anything and anyone is never random. You are not attending a dog show for no reason, you certainly aren't talking to me by chance. But what I am saying right now will only make sense once you find the reason why that is."
- "Great", after *Darth Vader* the panting shrink, I'm now in the presence of *Dog Yoda*. I thank Kiko for her wisdom; "I shall endeavour to dig further for the meaning of our encounter," I promise.
- "Figure it out, you'll be glad you did. Remember that how we conduct ourselves matters more than wining. Winning is only winning if you've won with integrity without hurting others, yourself included. Any other way, winning is for losers."

This time, I thank her purposefully performing the Japanese ritual of sticking both hand palms upwards. Kiko has touched me and humbled me in more ways than I can number. I leave the wonderful trio after profusely thanking them for their hospitality and a true moment of wisdom, no longer craving a green tea bean cake. Processing what Kiko said, my brain scans my history, trying to find commonalities with Kiko and my past; the name *Ildiko* pops up, a lovely Hungarian young woman I met, when aged eighteen in Budapest. But nothing adds up. An announcement breaks my brain farts and mental wander, informing us that the jury is ready to declare the winners, provoking everyone to gather disorderly around the two podiums rewarding all categories. The entire venue turned austere, much like a religious mass when devotees await the pope to appear. The apprehension is palpable; some tip-tap their phones, others bite their nails, many vape, waiting for the *Master Announcer* to speak up and elect the show's new canine stars.

After a short crowd warm-up, the jury begins to awards prizes for *best trick* to three contenders who were made to climb onto the podium, blissfully unaware of the crowd's cheerful clapping. I feel like I should do more to commune with the moment, although at that point, my mind is still busy processing Kiko's words. Winners of various categories are announced, their owners delighted with their medals, one gold medallist in particular acts as if she won't leave the podium until staff members gently usher her out of the way for the next category award. Next comes the *waggiest tail* award crowd with dogs rushing in, all around the podium as if they had been fed crack cocaine for the occasion. I stand near a larger-than-life, larger than average lady wearing an XXL t-shirt, and a *Essex Kennel Club* hat. She compulsively grinds tortilla chips which she scoops out by the dozen from an -also XXL- bag. She seems to be having a ball and even by my ogre eating standards, she takes the biscuit, bun intended -I mean pun-. I wonder how many scoops it is going to take for her to clean out her *Dorito* pile and whether or not she'll take breaks to siphon the giant soda can (ironically branded *Diet* Coke) sitting on her lap. The announcer breaks my inner gossip to inform us that "*Dylan the Villain*" has just won the UK *crufts* contest, obviously a crowd pleaser given the ensuing unanimous torrent of applause. That prompts *Lady Shrek* to shout out "I knew it, come on boy!" and look at me with a grin, as if I were her in on it accomplice. Curious enough to know what I missed, I confess to this is being my first (and last) dog show, which I hope will legitimise my absence of enthusiasm. Between two intimidatingly wide mouthfuls shovelled down, she explains, the white and brown coated winner was a *Papillon*, a breed named after the butterfly shape formed by their delicate long-haired ears. About to ask what *cruft* is, I realise that Dorito bits have shot out of her big mouth, hitting my neck, others landing on my shoe. I decide to cut my losses and defer to Google to find out everything about *cruft* and spare myself a second round of corn chip crumb raffle.

Meanwhile, more strangely worded awards are announced, leading to mixed reactions graded on their popularity till the top two awards come; *best groomed* and *best six legs* show. At that point, everyone has gathered around the contestants, gathered around the jury, gathered around the podiums. All background noise has stopped even the Dorito grinding *Lady Ogre* silently sips her Coke, eyes riveted on the jury, like everybody else. The jury finally breaks the silence: "Winners for best grooming are *Walnut* in third, *Kiko* in second and *White Oyster* in first place!" The crowd exults as the three winners and their trainers run up to the podium. I am gutted for Kiko not taking first prize, her owners look thrilled. Meanwhile, the bronze medal winner –clearly not an adept of Kiko's *winning matters less than how you participate* philosophy- looks unequivocally devastated. The announcer finishes with the long-awaited winners for *best six legs*, silencing the entire venue. I cross my fingers for Kiko to win. She doesn't. An impossibly cute cotton candy swirl-looking white *bichon frisé* named *Cloudy Clafouti* wins *Best in Show*. The hair ball on legs performs an acclaimed victory lap led by its owner, a tall stylish lady wearing a hard cap, a white crisp shirt, tucked in tight white trousers, also tucked in high black boots. No need to be a dog show dress code expert to spot that this lady is dressed out of sort for the event. She looks odd enough for metaphysics enthusiasts to entertain the idea that she could have slipped in a temporal fault where she was due to attend an equestrian event and ended up here instead. The contrast between the cartoonish fluffy loveliness of her bichon frisé with her stern and stiff military demeanour couldn't be more flagrant. More evidence in support of my *complementarity* theory by which, owners pick their dog for traits they crave. To me, this woman craves her dog's lightness of being, something she clearly doesn't allow to herself. The deluge of enthusiasm *for* the *Best in Show* winner announcement has left me indifferent. Although I slightly feel as an impostor crashing a party where I don't belong, meeting Kiko, the Japanese poodle and their lovely owners justifies my presence at the show, for which I have after all, bought my ticket like everybody else. That's when it hits me; Kiko is no less than the mirror of *Kyoko*, the very first woman I fell in love with, aged fifteen. Kyoko was a Paris based young

Japanese assistant to Mr Yoshii, an uber wealthy prominent Tokyo art dealer who owned a gallery in Paris that sold my uncle's paintings. That is how I had met her, in Paris, then in the south of France where I lived, when her boss came touring the French Riviera. Mr *Yoshii* was a self-made gigamillionaire and a giant arsehole who developed an interest in the art world. Being a shrewd businessman, he had hired a team of sophisticated art professionals to run his art business. Regrettably, his well-rounded entourage had not rubbed off on him and he remained the unfiltered ruthless man he always was. Once, we were in St Tropez, and he demanded Kyoko went onboard a yacht to ask the owners how much they wanted to be bought out and give him custody of the boat, on the spot. Luckily, for everyone, Kyoko had managed to talk him out of it, remaining calm and composed, throughout the handling of yet another whim from *baby Yoshii* who didn't get a new toy that day. Later on, he made her pay for her insubordination and after a few more years of coping with the psychopathic abuse she eventually resigned.

Kyoko was thirteen years older than I was and she had no idea whatsoever that during the little time we spent together, I marvelled at her every move, as a caveman discovering fire. Obviously, our relationship remained platonic due, I thought, to eight hundred kilometres and thirteen years between us, but really, due the fact that I was a delusional infatuated underaged with someone who was just being a caring friend. Although, come to think of it, who writes six-page letters to a fifteen-year-old? A foreigner practicing her French I suppose. She had been kind enough to give me her address, so we could correspond by letters. Every time I saw a letter in the mail with her beautiful handwriting on the envelope, my heart pounded, and an adrenaline rush inundated my brain. I would hope there would be more than a page to read. And there always was. Kyoko displayed effortless elegance, in most things she did, including crafting these letters, which I treasured. Writing this chapter brought fresh memories and interrogations to the extent of giving me the impetus to trace and reconnect with my very first flame. A thorough online search led me to Kyoko and only three days later, we were meeting in Paris. Thirty years had passed; I was forty-six and she was approaching sixty.

-

We met outside a café, hugged, walked a bit before sitting in a bistrot. During the first ten minutes, I made my overdue post-mortem love declaration which we laughed off and started catching up properly. After a brief pause, out of the blue, Kyoko discloses:
- "I love dogs."
- "You do?" I replied, not yet connecting the dots between her unprompted comment and the fact that what drove me to rekindle was writing a book about dogs in which she came back to my mind through *Kiko the Poodle*.
- "I do. I live on my own and it's a bit daunting, I always loved dogs, so I am thinking of getting one to keep me company."
- "Do you have a breed in mind?" I asked, my mind awoke this time, thinking how bizarre it would be, if it were a poodle.
- "Definitely a poodle." she replies, "they are my favourite dogs. I worry about leaving the dog alone all day though."

I am astonished. I tried to tamper the oddness of it all gently with some fun fact dropping.
- "You must know that poodles are all the rage in Tokyo. Is it why you set your eyes on one?"

She had no idea. By now, I felt comfortable enough to share about the book I was writing and why she was in it. I pulled up my laptop, to show her the chapter about *Kiko*, explaining that it led to our rekindling and that combined with the strange serendipitous poodle connection, it had to be a good omen for her to get one; "Get yourself a poodle Kyoko" I urged her. She reacted with a subdued laugh and delivered a measured response characteristic of her personality.

After a most pleasant evening we parted, I never saw Kyoko again, but we kept in touch, this time via texting, the days of waiting for an envelope via the mail having long gone. My heart was no longer pounding when hearing from her, however I was eager to receive a text at some point, letting me know that she had gone to the pet store to get a poodle of which I would see a picture attached to the text. I knew she would. And the text did come through. She got herself a cat instead. A cat she named Anubis, after the Egyptian deity.

Go figure…

プードル

9. HEART-WARMING ICE

If there ever was a dog who positively changed my mind about dogs it was *Ice*, a Labrador retriever, starring in a *Netflix* series about the dog-owner bond, super creatively titled *"DOGS"*. The episode featuring Ice portrays the life of the *Bellagio* family, owner of a centenary restaurant standing on stunning lake Como and open for business six months a year, during the warmer seasons. Ten-year old Ice is the inseparable companion of Alessandro, head of the family, to whom Netflix cleverly assigned the handling of the Italian voiceover throughout the episode. Alessandro is a lifelong fisherman in his mid-fifties who spends most of his time (and the most time) with Ice. The two of them spend most days fishing in the lake and bring back trout, perch and *lavarello* (a local white fish) to be stored, prepared, cooked, and served at the restaurant. For Alessandro, Ice is far more than a fishing mate and a family member; he is the family's heart, no less. What particularly stroke me was how he talks about his dog, as a proud parent would, of a child who went on to win a Nobel prize. As a Labrador retriever, Ice's hunting and drug sniffing top skills are barely used, but his endurance and dedication to the job was a force to be reckoned with. Wired like a rescue dog, he indulged in relaxing only once he made sure that everyone in the family was safe and accounted for, by way of a ritual that consisted in methodically checking on each member of the household. Like some sort of gentle retired special force agent. Alessandro describes Ice as the ideal fishing companion and hopes to stay by his side, fishing or not, as long as he is able and willing. He never presses Ice to join a fishing trip; instead, he drives him to the harbour, gets the boat ready and just wait, hoping for Ice to hop on from the deck. And he always does, unless something is off. We can hear the fisherman's voiceover express his heart-felt gratitude towards Ice with humility and respect, while images of Ice moving about are running. His eyes ooze kindness and, I could swear, an air of loyalty and commitment to his family. It warmed my heart. I hadn't felt this way in ages. It's as if I could feel the healing power of a creature that can be trusted unconditionally, perhaps because it was not human. Watching Ice made me aware of the absence of such warmth in my life. And looking at Alessandro and his family, I can't picture them without Ice. Despite being a *stoicism* adept, I envied what they had. As Alessandro said, Ice is the gel, if not the soul of the family. To think that a pet was the keystone of a household could feel far-fetched and yet, looking at them provided ample evidence to wear down one's scepticism, mine included. This extraordinary bond forged between humans and dogs seeded a new theory: for humans, such bonds are the result of the promise of little to no disappointment. And faith in such promise was possible *precisely* because it was found in a non-human creature. I bet that if I could twist Alessandro's arm into openly admitting whether he found Ice or his spouse to be more reliable he'd pick his dog. I heard enough adults claim they'd rather spend time with pets than with people. As a Buddhist monk once said: "*spend enough time with anyone and eventually, they'll disappoint you, and you'll resent them for it*". There's a theory I came to find depressingly infallible over time. As the say goes '*expectation is resentment under construction*'.

A life free of resentment resulting from unmet expectations is unheard of; even the wisest man or woman feels it at some point. It would be just about manageable if we didn't feel the urge to blame someone, sometimes ourselves, but preferably anyone else, for these setbacks born out of badly managed expectations (verbalised or not). Don't get me wrong; we blame ourselves all the time for petty things; but not the stuff that truly matters to us and that we should actually inspect; the stuff that hurts. Thus, over time, rather than admitting to our psychological frailty, we settle for minimal disappointment, and we call it wisdom. I clicked off this short film with a knot of sadness in the stomach for Alessandro and his family, knowing that at some stage they'll have to adapt to life without Ice. Being so taken, and an Italian speaker, I thought, why not follow through on my emotional impulse and get in touch? Before I knew it, I had called the *Mella* restaurant in San Giovanni and was on the phone with Rosy, Alessandro's wife and co-owner of the family business. After introducing myself and apologising for my half-broken Italian, I explain how touched I was by the *Netflix* documentary, how it enlightened my self-help journey thanks to its insight into the dogs-masters bond. I ask if at some point, I could come down to Como to meet them and of course, with *Mister* Ice. Rosy sounds surprised but delighted, we promptly agree on a date, and she even insists on booking my hotel for me. Thus, about a month later, after a painless flight to Milan Malpensa airport from London, I drive towards lake Como onboard a rental Fiat sticking to itinerary tips that Rosy was kind enough to email. After a ride of just over an hour, I reached San Giovanni, a splendid sun basked hamlet where I quickly find my way to the *Rosa dei Venti,* the hotel where I am booked for two nights. It looks like one of those picturesque fairy tale pads. I check in, freshen up and come back downstairs, ready to head for the *Mella* restaurant. The hotel receptionist asks if I need anything before wishing me a good day, I asked if she knows of Ice, the famous Netflix Lab retriever.

- "Of course, everyone knows Ice here; he's more famous than the mayor," the lady jokes, "Rosy told me about you; the gentleman who came all the way from London to meet Ice."

I nod, she seems chaffed and lets me know that Ice is no less than *l'anima dell villagio,* the soul of the village. After trading a few more niceties and smiles, I head towards Mella on foot, feeling more relaxed than I care to notice, and somewhere I had been before. Not a *déjà vu* per se, but really comfortable and familiar. The *soul of the family,* the *soul of the village*...Ice sure seems like a special one. The stroll to the restaurant by the glittering lake and mountains fading in in the background is a live slideshow of breath-taking views. I wonder if Ice is going to be around, perhaps greet me. He isn't. As soon as I reach the restaurant, I instantly recognise Rosy outside. We trade warm Mediterranean greetings; she popped out after the hotel receptionist had called to let her know I was on my way. She ushers us inside for some coffee, as you do in the *mecca* of the Espresso. I'm urged to sit around a lovely antique wooden white clothed table, just as I remembered the restaurant setting from watching the show. Rosy comes back with *espressi* and a tray of *cornetti* which I wholeheartedly acknowledge but decline to touch, to abort a sudden binge attack on them, something that a cornetto can trigger in the mad eater inside. I mentally bang the *'you never get a second chance to make a first impression'* mantra to focus solely on the exquisite espresso, so good, I wish it were a double. It reminds me that part of the tasting experience goes beyond product and expertise (percolated world-class coffee in this case) and that setting, and company matter just as much. I'm so present, I forgot why I'm here, as Rosy effortlessly practices the art of small talk. That's when Ice walks in. He notices me, comes around to check out the new visitor and goes to another room.

- "Here he is. *Il Maestro*" Rosy comments. "For once, he didn't go fishing. The last trip brought plenty of fish so today's will be a short one."
- "I was under the impression that Ice always went fishing with Alessandro?" I enquire.
- "Almost. Every blue moon, he doesn't, when he knows the trip will be short as is the case today, or if bad weather looms in which case, he warns him."
- "That's incredible! I thought cats could sense the bad weather coming. Dogs too?"
- "I don't really know about dogs, but we know that this one does. And he is never wrong!"

Intrigued by Ice, but now tortured by the sight of the *cornetti*, I ask if I could get some privacy to spend time with Ice before Alessandro gets back. Permission instantly granted, Rosy brings Ice over, goes to the kitchen to bring me another espresso.

- "I made it a double, I figured you might want extra caffeine after the flight."
- "You read my mind! It is not so much the trip, it's the finest coffee ever, thank you so much!"
- "In that case, I order you to eat the *cornetti*, don't be shy."

Her blessing comes as a relief, though when it comes to *cornetti*, I never need any encouragement. My strategy to act civilised until she left the room has paid off; I am now on my own and can let *Shrek* run wild and devour the cream stuffed cones. I do so, as Ice shakes himself and circles several times before dropping to the ground. My mouth is in taste bud paradise, my prefrontal cortex orgasming. I'm ready to speak to Ice. Or take a nap. I feel at home. No need to break the ice to speak with Ice. I open my mouth, the back of which still bathing in divine glucose and a splash of fine espresso, the edges covered in cream:

- "I know a lot about you already Ice, you know."
- "Is it the moving images on the box?" asked Ice referring to the Netflix show featuring him.
- "Yes. I watched it four times."
- "Is that why you are here?"
- "Yes, it is. To meet you."
- "What about my family?" Ice enquires with a look which, out of nowhere, makes me tearful. I can't help thinking about the gaping hole he'll leave the day he is gone.
- "Of course, in fact, it was the way Alessandro talks about you that shook me to the point of wanting to meet you all" I explain wiping teardrops across my face.
- "What does he say?"
- "Mostly mundane things about stuff the two of you get up to, mainly fishing. It's not what he says, but how he speaks of you."
- "Why does it matter?"
- "I guess we all wish for someone to feel about us the way Alessandro feels about you."
- "Haven't you got someone like that in your life, where you come from?"

Caught by surprise, I pause to regroup and pause some more to think before saying:
- "I want to say yes, but I don't think so. I don't handle praises well so, I tend to dismiss them."
- "Do you think your voyeuristic self has come here, or are you just curious to take a closer look at what you're unable to receive when it is given to you?"

By now, I've gotten used to being challenged and dispensed free psychoanalysis by the canine intelligentsia, and so, I dodge the tone but not the question:
- "Perhaps both, Ice. I could be trying to learn how to do that, but be unaware of it?" I offer.
- "It's the easiest thing" he woofs, "you must choose to receive praises, respect, love and care from those who truly love you. Else, you end up hurting the very people who matter the most to you. As a result, you might gravitate towards less kind-hearted people even and life becomes strenuous. You won't like it. But you'll get used to it."

Inadvertently -or not- Ice had just summarised the last two decades of my life.
- "Been there, done that my friend and you're right; I don't like it. At all. I hate it even."

Ice then drops a follow-up question I half expected:
- "Then why do it? Why let it happen?"
- "I suspect that's also why I'm here. To break a pattern," I venture, trying to look in control of why I sit there talking to a dog, my mouth half covered in *cornetto* cream and crumbs.
- "Well, break a leg breaking that pattern, but don't break a leg while fishing with us!" Ice asserts, with a dash of humour making the canine therapy session more digestible.

Under normal circumstances, I wouldn't take this seriously, but I haven't come all the way here to be my usual dismissive *Know-it-all* asshole.
- "Thank you, Ice" I humbly acknowledge.
- "Glad I can help!" he yaps back, tail wagging sideways "Can I tell you something else?"
- "Sure thing, please, go ahead Ice."
- "Have you just come out of prison?"
- "What? No... I've never been to prison. Why?"
- "Because you eat faster than a dog and we eat like pigs!" he explains, rolling his eyes and masticating in the air "Just saying!".

Delighted by the confrontation, which is nothing but constructive criticism, just like all my interactions with dogs so far, even Magnum, helped me conquer my fear of giant dogs which was no small feat. Shortly after our conversation, Alessandro shows up, back from the lake, and the two of us hit it off; he insists I come over for dinner. Later in the evening I meet with the rest of the family and dinner is a memorable experience wonderful, in its simplicity, something I realise is cruelly missing in my unnecessarily complex urban lifestyle that feels so often meaningless. After dinner, Ice is sprawled across Alessandro's lap, his sides rising and falling, his nose mashed against the ground in a most uncomfortable-looking manner. Dogs can sleep in peculiar positions. Alessandro won't let me return to the hotel without a last *sambuca* and committing to join him and Ice fishing in the morning, which I naturally do. Thus, the next morning, the three of us leave for the deck. It feels special, like we're about to perform a solemn ritual within Alessandro and Ice's sanctuary. And I don't belong in there. Concealing my feelings isn't an option so I share the view with Alessandro, that however grateful I am to be invited, I am content just hanging out by the deck and watch the spectacular surroundings until they return. Which I am, in a way. Both Alessandro and Ice look at me, summoning me onto the boat without a word, until I hop on, and we take off. Here I am, on the same boat I had seen on the *Netflix* show, with Alessandro and Ice! The experience is intense in its gentleness: I stopped thinking, despite being curious by nature I am not particularly eager to find out anything about the lake or the kind of fish that thrive in it, nor is Alessandro trying to engage in a conversation. Unlike me, he and Ice know when to speak. I try to learn, watching the two silent teachers. The mesmerising light beams over the radiant landscape as the boat slices through the lake at medium speed. Taking in the meditative dimension of this fishing experience is what I came here for, on a small boat in the company of a dog and a stranger who happens to be a very private man and yet opened his home, his privacy to me, as if to honour my effort to try to figure out whatever I came here to do, no questions asked; my getting on a plane seems good enough a reason. A realisation begins to sink in; as Ice inferred, I should strive to welcome this act of respect for what it is; kindness, compassion, brotherly love, the love I so often reject for fear of accepting it. I'm not one to sit in a Tibetan monastery waiting to *receive the light*. I believe in humans who teach other humans, simply by being who they are. I keep quiet, letting the excruciatingly alien feeling of joy violate my psyche, exchanging regular looks with Alessandro and Ice, who I hope, are unaware of teardrops bubbling behind my thick shades, as we fend off the waters of timelessness.

Eventually we fished, reeled in a bunch of shiny fish of various sizes and colours from the beneath the surface of the lake and brought back a decent lot back to the *Mella*. I had the privilege to share another terrific meal, divinely cooked by Rosy and her daughter. Halfway through lunch, I noticed something unusual: I was eating at the same pace as everyone else at the table without purposely toning it down! I had adjusted to theirs. At that point, I had forgotten Ice's remark about my freaky eating manners, which meant that my behaviour adaptation had been purely unconscious. Being so relaxed around them had surely rubbed off on my grumpy single man habits. I wouldn't go as far as saying that I felt part of the family, but I felt serene enough and at home. Certainly, more at home than in my own. Lucky for all of us that their eating habits rubbed off on me, not the other way around!

Ice had brought to light the fact that if I could not accept love and praises, I stood little chances to forge healthy relationships in life. And he and his family triggered the profound realisation that I wanted to build one. Before I left San Giovanni, we took a few pictures of ourselves, one of which I framed and hung. It acts as a reminder of what home feels like, when wandering aimlessly on my own, in my own.

10. THE GREYHOUND IN MY NIGHTMARE

For over two decades, I have had a recurrent dream featuring an eerie, grotty, lanky long-haired greyhound staring at me. In the nightmare-like dream he'd always, scare the life out of me. Sometimes he'd stand still and stare and other times, he'd move towards me, its legs still, as if transported towards me on an invisible flying carpet. And I couldn't move to run away from him. All I could do was stand still and be terrified.

One day, I saw the live carbon copy of that ghastly ghostly dog walk in one of the regular cafés I haunted in my neighbourhood. Naturally I felt instantly scared to my guts by the obviously harmless creature. I mustered up some courage and went up to the dog's owner, a middle-aged lady whose peaceful demeanour had probably encouraged me to do so. The woman didn't look one bit as the witch I would have pictured as the logical owner of the chilling greyhound from my nightmare. She politely listened to my babbling and was even kind enough to engage into a courtesy chat after introducing herself, as Patricia. I thus shared my fear of dogs and the recurrent nightmare specifically about hers "Lucky me!" Patricia joked. She carries on empathetically, sharing dog wisdom and tips -that I instantly forget- before bidding me good luck with dogs and a nice day. Patricia came across as open-minded, amicable, spiritual. Some two months later, I spot her again in Battersea park, walking the grotty greyhound by the pond. I go up to her, she remembers me. We chat about the serendipity of meeting again at a different time and place, I look at the dog of my nightmare glaring with no discernible expression. Patricia offers an opinion, to help, to get rid of me or to accomplish both of those goals: "sometimes emotions can crystallise into things and creatures. In your case a dog who bears a spooky resemblance to mine." That brings to mind a French comic book I used to read as a kid and portrayed *Pouik* (pronounced *pwick*) a dog identical to Patricia's. His name was peculiar enough for me to remember and I ask Patricia for her dog's name: it's Harry. Now, there is a name that had been tormenting me for months and triggers an enormous amount of resentment and anger! Moreover, it relates to a *Harry* I have never actually met, just like I had never met Patricia's greyhound. Both *Harrys* have been ghosts haunting my mind and triggering fear-based anger. Moreover Patricia's inspired comment led me to ask for her dog's name which led to quite an epiphany; to stop fearing the product of my imagination. What I find most peculiar is that we should meet twice in two months at two different locations, as if to get a second chance to ask for her dog's name, which I failed to do the first time. Also, had we met a year before, the name Harry wouldn't have meant anything then. I realise that paying attention to dogs can help understand my own psychological flaws and their underlying triggers, if I pay attention. I want to chat with Harry but don't know where to start, Patricia, suggests I touch him.

- "I realise how ridiculous that sounds, but I don't think I can do it yet. I appreciate your help though."
- "I understand." Patricia simply declares.

She does. I feel like a little girl, afraid of a dog who looks like the canine version of a Greek philosopher.

"Screw it," I hear myself say out loud. I lean to stroke the dog; no reaction whatsoever. Patricia hands its lead over to me, steps aside to take a call. I now feel compelled to speak to the scruffy dog.

- "Well, hello, *Pouik*. Not too hot with the long hair coat you have got on here?"
- "It's fine. And it's Harry, but you know that. Why don't we talk about your dream?" he offers cutting to the chase, "I heard your conversation. It's rather odd that you've been dreaming of me for decades, and here I am."
- "Well, I have been dreaming of *a* dog who looks just like you" I correct, "but yes, it is odd, since you really are its spitting image."
- "Tell me something; you told Patricia that at times I stand still and that at other times I make a move towards you; when I am still, are you able to walk away from me?"
- "Good question. I freeze every time, no matter what you do, I mean, what *the dog*, does."
- "I see. So, whether or not the object of your fear is getting closer to you, you are unable to do anything about it. Would you agree?"
- "I don't see how I can disagree, but I'm not a shrink. Are you implying, or trying to make me realise that I am not one to face his fears?"
- "You said it, not I," Harry relies with a sneer.
- "I can't believe it, I am being patronised once again, by yet again another…"
- "Dog?" the dog interrupts.
- "Well, yes."
- "Considering that…." this time I interrupt him.
- "I know what you're going to say; considering our conversation is an imaginary projection of my unconscious to process my fear of dogs and apparently, other fears too, feigning

indignation to be lectured by a dog is just escapism to avoid dealing with the underlying issue. Right, *Aristotle*?"
- "All I have to say is that if everyone progressed as much as you do by conjuring up self-therapy through imaginary conversations, therapists would be running out of business. By the by, how scared of me are you now?"
- "Not at all" I realise.

Patricia has hung up and came back. However pleasant I find her company I don't know whether the feeling is mutual and feel fairly sure that I've learnt the lesson I was supposed to learn. I say goodbye, jokingly adding that the three of us will probably meet again a third time if we are meant to. Patricia amicably nods in agreement with a smile.

We never met again.

11. THE ONE WHOSE DEATH I GRIEVED

A few years ago, Natasha, a great soul I had grown very fond of unexpectedly lost *Baloo*, her beloved dog. I never met him and only saw pictures of -the appropriately named- Baloo, who did look like the legendary *Jungle Book* bear. Baloo was a gigantic furry dog who resembled a bear but who was the least frightening creature who ever lived. He was the gentlest of the gentle giant family who everybody needed in their life. Possibly even me...

It is obvious that Baloo reminded me of the St Bernard I was sat on top of as a toddler and had terrified me. But nothing scared me about Baloo. Possibly because I only saw photos of him but more so because I found the kindness oozing from his eyes just transcendental. To me, he was an angel, posing as a bear, posing as a giant dog. Glancing at his pictures had even brought closure to the childhood trauma that the *Grizzly Bear* St Bernard of the Italian mountains had put me through. Out of respect and pudor for Baloo, I decided to not transcript any of my text exchanges with Natasha after he passed, and during which, I was unable to find appropriate words to convey my sorrow, condolences, and support.

But I will say that the glimpse I captured of the love Natasha felt for her dog was enough to shatter my heart. It *was* unconditional love.

12. THE ONE WHOSE DEATH I CHEERED

I had moved to Zurich, Switzerland right before the 2008 crisis. Being self-employed in the private equity industry, I ended up in a tough spot scrambling for money when the financial meltdown hit. It led me to work for a severely insane psychopath. He managed a small team running commodity equity funds out of Zug, a renowned tax evasion den outside Zurich. There were also small offices in Cape Town and in the *city* of London, where I aspired to return. This jovial son of a Nazi *capo* was a caricature of the now proverbial *pervert narcissist*, better described as a giant arsehole and a specimen, disproportionately represented in the financial services industry. He wasn't the loud obvious type who revealed himself; he was the vicious snaky kind, professing to be a philosopher for whom over-achieving and being number one at everything he undertook was merely a rewarding side effect of a balanced lifestyle lived in complete humility. Yuck! My job was to build new markets from scratch by bringing fresh institutional money into the three funds that had endured a near death experience following the 2008 massive asset exodus (called *outflows*) when global financial markets collapsed. I found myself working out of a converted house in Zug, a village so quiet, that it gave me perspective when thinking of Zurich as the *land of the dead*, after spending a decade in London. The pathologically insecure control freak I worked for was on his fourth failing start-up fund and third lawsuit battle with previous associates. Despite him being the obvious common thread of the three fiascos, he'd plough through, convinced he was the victim, a misunderstood humble business leader, too smart and too ethical for his own good. And he was none of those attributes. He was full of shit, full of himself and he was his best customer. A dealer getting high on his own supply. *Donald Trump* with an education. He ruled through intimidation and every single trick from the pervert narcissist's book which he could have written himself, had he had any self-awareness and writing talent. Anyone with an emotional quotient higher than a cucumber's could deduct the impact of his gruesome Nazi heritage. His aptitude to look at you in the eyes, with his wide open to try to make you feel small was chilling and worked with most of the staff. It didn't work on me. He didn't make me feel smaller, but the scumbag repelled me. And the feeling was mutual. In the tepid wake of the financial crisis, market and working conditions were to put it mildly, challenging. But *Shitler*, as we dubbed the horrible boss, did the one thing that would make my day job a living nightmare; he brought his fucking dog to the office. The barking kind. The stupid kind. The stupid barking kind. I instantly transferred all the scorn I felt for his owner onto it. Half of my office time was spent on the phone, persuading European money managers to invest in funds they had never heard of, amidst Shitler's mop-looking pet (another mop) intermittent loud barking. To endure such ordeal, you had to be either a co-dependent masochist, which his fanatic PA was, or dead broke, which I was. One morning I heard that the mop (whose name I forgot, blocked off my mind due to PTSD) was struck dead by an illness. I'd be lying if I said that I felt sorry for his demise. I felt elated. The relief brought by the end of the ordeal of constant high pitch barking far outweighed any heartfelt sympathy.

When I found out that *Shitler* was considering getting a new dog for the office, I went into his, to plead for delaying this maddening idea at least until the summer holiday, to grant me two solid months of uninterrupted work, before markets cooled down and everyone jetted off to the sunshine. He neither agreed nor disagreed. He kept it vague as pervert pricks do. He did not get a new dog, at least by the time I left this company, and he fell out with management who took him to court, on his fourth flurry of lawsuits.

It was hard to tell if *Shitler* made a point of not showing any emotion in the face of his pet's demise or if he did not feel any. Since I didn't care either, it made me wonder how much of a psychopath I was, myself. In hindsight, however, had I known of Baloo at the time (Natasha's adorable giant love ball), the debate would have been settled and the thought wouldn't have crossed my mind; my empathy undoubtedly extends to animals, if I either like them and/or their owners.

This painful Swiss chapter taught me that, if someone triggered enough disgust in me, I could be as heartless as I found them to be in return.

13. BETTY AND POPPY

Poppy is a *Yorkshire terrier* and a medical dog trained to react to her owner's insulin and blood sugar level swings. Her owner, Philippa is a neighbour living on my street. She relies on Poppy's hyper vigilance and natural radar, to alert her in time every time she needs a shot. Poppy is so special, she even featured on a *BBC* TV show as a super smart *Yorkie* with a sixth sense, who yaps faster than Philippa's medical sensor can beep to let her know when her health needs attention. Poppy and I clicked immediately, love at first woof. She is tiny, clean, her fury fluffy head makes her skinny body look disproportionately small. With large black eyes and large perked ears, she looked like a *Gremlin,* an opinion echoed by many, as an online search for *Yorkie Gremlin* testifies. There is an evident flair of intelligence about her; she'd stand still, perked ears, staring at you with an intimidating *I know things about you that you don't* piercing look. One day, I startled everyone familiar with my aversion to dogs, by posting a picture of Poppy and I cuddling on my couch. I had volunteered (not accepted; vol-un-tee-red) to take custody and care of her at mine for three days, while Philippa stayed in Brussels for an extended weekend. During our time together, Poppy looked after me as much as I looked after her. I quickly gained her favours by ditching the dry food I was supposed to feed her for home-made slow-cooked omelette, that she devoured while keeping her aristocratic composure. I admired her eating of the sort and hoped that perhaps one day, I too, could look aristocratic when food binging. Mutual cuddling quickly became mutually abundant.

The look in her eyes was so thought provoking and stimulating, I didn't need to gauge for the right time to start a conversation; I talked to her all the time. On our second day, she and I were on the couch where we spent most of our time together when I said:
- "I wish I'd met you earlier *Pops*, who knows, it might have helped tamper my dog aversion."
- "You feel that way around me because I'm me, I doubt you'd be this keen on other Yorkies, let alone other dogs." She's right.
- "So then, Pops, I would be so drawn to you because of your personality, is that it?"
- "Pretty much, woof."
- "I like you so much coz how smart I find you."
- "That, my hyper vigilance, alertness, sense of duty and my ability to read people's needs."
- "Not humility?" I joke. She stares waiting for me to move on. "Ok... Why these attributes?"
- "We like in others what we wish we had or what we 've already got. You're drawn to me coz I am awesome but also, because I am you."

Most dogs I had encountered turned out to remind me of someone who had an impact on my psyche. But Poppy implies that she would be a *mini-me* would have to be deeply unconscious on my part, considering the strong negative bias I inflict upon any introspection and self-analysis. Self-praise is not my forte.

Poppy looks up, as if to draw my attention, letting me know she has more to say:
- "I can also see myself in you. You care, you give, you're so perceptive as to effortlessly address people's unspoken needs. That's one of the reasons why people find you popular and are drawn to you...How am I doing?"

- "Well... Since it's just you and I, I would say that you are describing me better that I ever could... Or ever dare, Pops", I confess, in a rare moment of self-praise, away from the lights of fake humility.
- "Are you aware that you are a mystic and a healer?"

I became a hypnotherapist to help people. So, I nod, hesitantly, but I do nod.

- "I sense that you only tap into the tip of your iceberg potential. I see many overestimate their capacities but being far less resourceful than they imagine. The opposite is true about you. You ought to become aware of that."
- "You're not saying that because I feed you exquisite omelette, are you?" I tease, falsely suspicious.
- "You know I'm not. But I won't lie, I'll miss them when Philippa returns," Pops admits, her eyelids lowering in slight disarray.
- "These are kind words Poppy"
- "You'd be wise to and even wiser to do something about it," she insists, with one of her mystical stares that she holds until she gets a reaction.
- "Well, on my mum's side, the family has a history of clairvoyance and mediumship. That sort of thing..."
- "There we go...Put it this way; how many people do you think speak with dogs the way you do? Dog lovers talk to us all the time, but we don't talk back because they won't listen. We're just a conduit through which they feel good about themselves. On the other hand, you speak to us to better yourself. You ask good questions...Most of the time..."

- "Pops, you do realise that our conversations aren't real, right? I mean, no psychic power there...And how is what I am doing, also not a selfish enterprise, only for different reasons?"
- "Who are you to say that a conversation happening in your mind isn't real?" That oddball somehow hits the bullseye and shuts me up. "You may not like dogs, but you get out of your way to face the uncomfortable. Why downplay the magnitude of what you do?"
- "Okay... What is it exactly that I'm doing,?"
- "Just imagine if people faced their fears instead of rotting in shells where cognitive bias grow into monsters. That's how wars start; traumas leading to misunderstandings, to core beliefs, then generalisation, and ultimately mass antagonism."
- "I see... So... You think I could be the next *Gandhi*, or something, Pops?" I joke, at a loss for words and agile thinking.
- "I don't know who Ghandi is," Pops replies, her inquisitive look on, eyes wide open and perky ears. "Is he/she dead?", she asks, rolling on her back, and doing impressions of a corpse!
- "You do make me laugh, Pops! He was a figure famous for leveraging non-violence to accomplish his life mission....," I tentatively explain.
    - "Bit like Jesus then. I see...I think you are more like a truth seeker whose consciousness elevates in the process. And you should share that. You guys read books. Write a book or something."

And with that, I turned my notes into this book.

The only other dog I ever met who came close to Poppy was Betty. A shelter dog, adorning a short-haired shiny black coat, who despite her humble background, looked like a noble knight and royalty. I had met her way before I met Poppy, when I was around sixteen years old in the French countryside. Resilience was her strongest suits. Her upbringing had been opposite to Poppy's cushy life. Betty was a survivor, abused, ambushed and abandoned on the road and abused again until being rescued and sheltered by my friend's family. She was a gorgeous mixed-race breed with striking, soul piercing green eyes that told a story of astonishing spirit and resilience. However, her most characteristic trait was kindness. She could have been *Baloo's* sister from another mother. Her kindness was not blissful and unaware, but rather the result of a conscious decision made, despite, and in the face of the world's dread and insanity. Betty would never act kind: she *was* kind...or she wasn't. Her sheer presence would alter the tone of voices and the course of a conversation in a room. She had the gravitas of a Shakespearean actor but freed of the exasperating ego. Her noble decent demeanour was carved in painful life experiences and carried a defiance that can sometimes be observed with holocaust survivors who managed to grow out of the horror they were put through. I loved that dog; I just didn't realise it at the time. In fact, to me, she never was a dog; she was Betty. She was *my Ice*. Just like the Bellagio family in Lake

Como saw Ice as a family member who happened to be a dog. If I had to project myself onto dogs, as dog owners do, it would have been onto Poppy, for her crazy brain and nursing skills and onto Betty, for her resilience and her kindness.

Two epiphanies hit me with that reflexion. One was a classic case of projection: the fact that specific dog behaviour, looks and attributes would trigger feelings directly associated to people I had met throughout the course of my life. The second, the narcissism that deploy when channelling feelings towards non-human creatures; if we created *God* to our image, we also try to either make our *Dog* to our image or pick one incarnating attributes we aspire to have. Thus, an obese owner would tend to choose a larger dog or a skinny one, but rarely an average sized dog, short individuals would get a small dog or a tall one but rarely an average sized one. If projection and compensation were substantial factors behind the dog frenzy, could it be because dogs were the most malleable creatures to project onto and mould to the image constructed by our subconscious?

An event I could not foresee was about to fast-track my search, bring more answers than I had bargained for and just like that, change the course of my life.

14. SPIRIT ANIMALS AND ANIMAL SPIRIT

Susana has the coolest and the strangest job I know of, to this day; she describes herself as a *white witch* and *vortex* therapist. After graduating in psychology in her twenties, she left for South America, where she spent time with Shamans and became one herself. She also mastered the art of pendulum reading, tuning forks handling, *chakras* healing and clairvoyance. She became a shamanic therapist with highly developed psychic abilities. A decade into her journey, she had created her own method, and when we met, she was into her third decade as a spiritual healer. Susana was atypical, esoteric, funny, energetic, and powerful. She was accurate, precise and didn't sugar coat the messages she channelled nor their interpretations. She steered clear from the caricatural new age wishy washy pitfalls; she was a witch, a good *witch*, and a *good witch*; she was a good *good witch*. She was the real deal. And a real witch…

The shamanic session I had under her guidance was one of the greatest experiences and lessons of humility I ever received. I met her in session as a patient of mine and afterwards, Susana offered to return the favour with a *vortex therapy* session. I certainly wasn't going to say *no* that! A week later, she shows up at my place, equipped with a small rolling suitcase packed with various artefacts, many of which I am seeing for the first time; volcanic stones, other stones, obsidian crystals, other crystals, tuning forks, *Florida* water, white sage leaves and a pendulum. Lucky that Susana is a likeable character who inspires confidence and around whom I feel relaxed and comfortable…

We start off with an unusual *Q&A* session for Susana to carry out her *psychic detective investigation*, which she conducts following her pendulum swings. She dwells on a particular period of my life: "What happened when you were seventeen? You haven't said enough. I am missing pieces of your *life jigsaw* that year." To my surprise, we retrieve a myriad of significant events that year, which I had blanked out of my mind, while Susana takes note. After nearly an hour she pieces together my psycho-portrait, connecting dots to establish patterns of uncanny resonance. We then begin the shamanic *seance*, I lay on my couch, Susana patches half a dozen small semi-transparent stickers on my arms and torso. With my head resting and my eyes closed, she begins striking a pair of tuning forks (from seven sets; each corresponding to one of the seven chakras) at the edge of my eardrums. The forks vibration rapidly plunges me into a modified state of awareness and hear myself say that '*I am recalibrating*'. I'll find out, that the stickers patched on me are called *recalibration cards* and were carefully applied according to answers provided during the preliminary *psychic investigation* phase! In session, I experience odd swings, from feeling anchored to as if my torso had split, creating a sensation of elevation and of profound well-being. Susana utters the word *transmute* several times and keeps on striking various tuning forks, taking me to a state of evanescence, with visions fuzzing through my mind, as the smell of burnt white sage fills the entire room. She carries on with the ritual, placing a volcanic stone on the palm of each of my hands, which I instinctively wrap in both fists and gently lay on top of my closed eyelids, as if I my eyes had become the large, round black stones.

A few incantations and *Florida water* sprays over my laid body later, the session comes to a slowdown. I open my eyes and regain most of my senses. I sit up on the couch and inform Susana that I need the bathroom.

- "Hurry back, I must clock you up," she warns.

There is an odd statement that immediately makes sense the second I stand on my feet, as I tilt and swing sideways, as if I became an organic accordion. It feels as if I am *open in half*.

- "Wow! I see what you mean...You do need to...clock me up, as you say."
- "Nothing to worry about; you must be feeling a little out of kilter. To work on your main chakras I need them wide open. And now I need to zip you up, for you to anchor and properly realign."

I feel exactly as she described. And thus, I head to the bathroom. As soon as I walked in, I think to myself *"you are not alone in here,"* a thought promptly replaced with; *"you are alone, but you are not yourself."* I am in my flat, in my bathroom, familiar territory, but I feel out of sort. Once I proceed to wash my hands, I peek at myself in the mirror and instead of my face, I see ...a fucking lion's head! I am dazed but not scared, somehow, I look at this lion's face as if I were casually looking at another version of myself. Once I turn the tap off and reach for a towel, I look at myself in the mirror again to witness the lion's head dissipates and morph into that of a *Sphinx*, with two big black holes in the eye sockets! It is as if I *am* that black-eyed Sphinx. I will only make the connection with *placing* the black volcanic stones on my eyes in session, later. Few seconds later, I witness my face briefly transit through a man-feline hybrid hazy spectre and finally morph back into its usual look. Remarkably, I'm still unscared; I am high; as if I elevated onto a different, higher plan. I stumble out of the bathroom, Susana is waiting by the window, where she proceeds with the *zipping* ritual, that works like a charm. Within minutes, I feel grounded, in control, the notion of time has vanished. We sit at my dining table, where I laid some home cooked food for us to share while tea is brewing when Susana asks:

- "Did you see a lion?"

Though I'm as calm, cool, and collected as ever, her question comes as if a truck just hit me.

- "I did!" I stutter, "as I was in the bathroom...I saw a lion's head instead of mine...", I admit, "I was about to mention it."
- "That's uncommon, usually patients see their totem animals while in session, but I suppose you saw yours in the bathroom because I hadn't zipped you up yet. You were still in their realm, so to speak."
- "Well, this is obviously novelty to me... The lion's head felt so real, as real as my real face."

I am about to tell her about the *Sphinx* head when she cuts in.

- "And did you a see Sphinx? Or something that resembles a Sphinx, with two holes instead of eyes, or two huge black eyes?"

I don't scare easy but a chill runs through my bones.

- "I did... How do you, I mean, who are you?"
- "In session, I see my clients' spirit animals."
- "How? And what are spirit animals?" I ask.
- "They're also known as *totem* or *guide* animals. Their personality traits, behaviour and symbolism resonate with your core. We have

two, three core spirit animals and a few ancillary ones who come and go to help with specific life cycles, to deliver messages and guidance. Shamans channel those."
- "Shamans like yourself," I assert.
- "That's right. And, did you see a cobra?"
- "No cobra... No.... I haven't... Have you?"
- "I did, yes" she lets me know.

Susana then goes on to what she refers to as *closing the loop*, wrapping up the session by linking the meaning of my spirit animals to my psycho-spiritual portrait. The findings revealed by the *Lion*, *Sphinx* and *Cobra* symbolic are almost as staggering as seeing my face shape shift in my mirror and find out that Susana had seen them too. With no interpretation required, the symbolic of the three animals are a summary of my life and the portrait Susana drew in pre-session during the pendulum *Q&A* phase. It also addresses the missing pieces of the jigsaw that Susana has pieced together. I read various passages in disbelief, while Susana smiles, as if to let me know that all is well and unfolding according to a plan, that I have clearly not been made aware of. However, the loop feels *closed* indeed. I quit smoking that day and the next day, I felt grounded in a way I haven't felt before nor since. Diner is most interesting and before leaving, Susana recommends: *"Try to not see anyone tomorrow, you'll probably want to enjoy your own company. And tonight, don't be surprised if you experience vivid dreaming. Welcome it. Your spirit animals came out very powerfully. You seem ready to receive their messages, whatever they may be."* At that point, I'm no longer computing what she says and once she goes, I have a shower and go straight to bed, feeling amazing. That night, as Susana predicted, I have a vivid dream, being visited by no less than Betty, my beloved shiny short-haired black coated dog looking as stunning as ever staring at me with her mesmerising green eyes.

- "Betty…Am I dreaming? Can you see me?"
- "Of course, I can. I came here to see you and for you to see me" Betty naturally replies.
- "It has been so long. Why now?"
- "You summoned me."
- "I did…? Oh yes; I did!" I exclaim recollecting my shamanic session and connecting the dots. "Does that mean you're one of my *totem* animals? I mean, *spirit* animals?" I venture.
- "No but one of them came to me to let me know that you were ready. So here I am."
- "I didn't realise how much I had missed you, Betty. I am ready…? Ready for what?"
- "Ready to hear what I was brought here to make you understand. You took your time by the way…"
- "If I am ready, then please tell me, Betty Boo!"
- "Okay then."

She comes closer at eye level for our eyes to click and she plugs my mind into a film stream. I begin seeing familiar faces, even some of my talking dogs, I see, Higgins in Sweden, Blue the pug in London, Magnum the donkey in Philly, while Betty provides context through some sort of telepathic voiceover:

- "The journey you embarked on is inspiring; you got of your comfort zone and out of your own way to face your fears. Each canine conversation revealed that the underlying trigger is always someone other than the dog and sometimes even yourself. However, you've been barking up the wrong tree."

Am I really dreaming or am I semi-awake and still under Susana's shamanic influence? Also, has Betty intended the pun? I am confused. Betty senses that I want to intervene but stops me dead in my tracks. It's not time. It's time to look and listen.

"You have figured out that dog owners often project themselves onto their dogs. And you think that speaking with dogs will help you cure your fear of them. But you aren't afraid of dogs. Neither do you find them loud, dirty or disgusting. These are decoys and mental projections of your feelings towards specific people you resent, including at times, yourself."

Her words sink in, as pictures keep streaming; *Blue* who grossed me out because he reminded me of my sick teacher, *Magnum* who scared the hell out of me and reminded me of the German shepherd who rammed me out of my pram as an infant, *Kiko* who reminded me of Kyoko my very first crush, *Baloo* onto whom I projected my fondness for his owner, Shitler's dog onto whom I projected my hatred for his owner, *Poppy* and *Betty* who reminded me of myself, and *Grace*, the mop, because...why not, I guess.

- "You see...This whole thing is about you. Designed for you to see through your real fears, not your perceived ones. And face them."
- "What fears are they then, Betty?
- "Being less than, not being enough. And your fear of abandonment."
- "Is that so...? Don't understand how you got there."
- "Really...When you were rammed off your pram, how did you feel?" Betty questions.
- "I was an infant. I don't remember."

- "If you had to guess…"
- "I would say scared. Left alone."
- "And how would being left alone as an infant make one feel?"
- "I suppose, not secured, insecure, unsafe."
- "And how does that make you feel?"

  After a short pause, a flash springs to mind:

  "As if I was not worth of being looked after…Less than…I see what you mean now…Alright."
- "And when your stepdad sat you on that huge St Bernard in the Italian ski resort, when you were three years old; how did that make you feel?"
- "I was terrified. I could see that from the pictures they took. And I suppose it made me feel unsafe and not brave enough… Not enough… I see…"
- "Now, why did you have a stepdad? Where was your biological father?"
- "He was never there. He left before I was born."
- "And how does that make you feel?"

  Thinking isn't required to address a no brainer.
- "Abandoned."
- "See.. You pretext an aversion to dogs as a proxy to camouflage your fear of abandonment. You don't care one bit about dogs, one way or the other. But now that we unearthed it, you must face your fear."

I might not care about dogs, but I care about Betty though. That reminds me of a similar comment Blue made when he categorically discarded my contention that my aversion to dogs had to be linked to my infantile dog traumas.

- "Then, what am I doing this for? To get closure with my dad leaving and never reaching out?"
- "The first family who rescued me from the street was troublesome. The father was a heavy drinker and an abusive husband. He routinely slapped his wife and then began to beat me up for no reason, whenever he would get drunk, which happened a lot. I learnt that in life, the question to ask when facing violent behaviour is not *why the violence* but *why the pain*: what sort of pain could drive a man to behave of the sort with his wife and a dog? That is the question. And the answer, in his case, was that he had ran away from his family home aged fifteen to escape his abusive alcoholic father, who routinely beat him up and his mum every time he got drunk. And since human adults tend to become either the antithesis or a replica of their parents, this man became his raging alcoholic dad."
- "What happened to you then?"
- "I did the same thing he did when he was a teenager: I ran away from him."
- "How did you find out about his childhood?"
- "The same way I found out about your stepdad and your dad: using my psychic power."
- "Of course, you did, you're psychic" I comment in a nonchalant semi-conscious state.
- "And so are you," Betty added.
- "What? Psychic?"
- "Woof," she nods approvingly.

I won't challenge her, Poppy said the same thing.

- "So, then Betty, what is the parallel between the foster family man you ran away from and I? Are you saying that I have become...my mum...? Or my dad, who I don't even know?"

- "No. What I am saying is that this man refused to face the shame and the fury buried within and turned his rage against me and those who loved him the most. I'm saying that sometimes we choose the easier path of not facing our true fear, and find refuge in isolation, excess, violence. You chose to face your fears which is admirable. I just came here to make sure you face the right fear; the one and only fear that petrifies you in life."
- "That would be my dad abandonment issues."

The image slideshow has stopped and now all I can see is Betty's magnificent emerald eyes dispensing a silent elegant telepathic "*yes*". I can feel all the love and care in the world in her eyes, that it is high time I embraced, passing through me. The challenge, to accept the love I resisted all my life and which I always believed I didn't deserve. Because I have been left unattended in my pram and almost eaten alive by a German Shepherd who rammed me off it onto the ground. Because I was sat on a St Bernard when I didn't want to, by a stepdad who I didn't want either. Because I was left to my own device at a young age and wasn't given enough affection nor any guidance. Because of that, love had always terrified me if I encountered it. So, I alienated it before I could taste it, certain that it'd be taken away from me, as my biological father did by assisting in giving me life but no further acknowledgement. As Higgins feared that he could lose the love of his owners to another dog. Ice, Labrador retriever and guardian angel in Como was right; I had to finally accept to receive love and respect when it was given to me, if I wanted to put an end to a troublesome life, unnecessarily strenuous, complex, and complicated.

And so, I take a deep breath, making a conscious effort to dive into Betty's eyes and receive the love beaming out of them. The second I do, I sense instant relief, along joy and Betty's approval whose aura slowly envelops my mind, body, and soul. I cocoon in there. Blissfully. Am I dreaming? Am I dead? It doesn't matter. I feel home. At last. After a while that could have last a minute or an eternity, I feel the need to ask my green-eyed guardian angel one last question.

- "If one of my spirit animals summoned you to come to me why say that *I* summoned you?"
- "Because your spirit animals *are* you. So, you did summon me. Through the *sphinx* within."
- "Really? Wow, that's...so cool!"
- "Surely you remember placing the black stones upon your eyes in session, then seeing your face as a black-eyed sphinx in the bathroom?"
- "Of course, I remember. How can I forget?"
- "To signal that you and the sphinx are one."
- "That would explain why I wasn't scared during the phantasmagorical encounter. Why choose me Betty? I know why you came to me. But why me?"
- "We're soulmates. Just like you and Poppy. Everything is circular, soulmates are like chain links that find each other, click, connect, to share what's meant to be before parting."
- "It means you aren't staying around for long?"
- "I died a year ago, Axel. But I'm around in spirit. Now that you know, you can contact me through your *sphinx* spirit and I am pleased to say that next time we meet, it will be for cuddles, no more heavy stuff. Coz now, you can be with the one."
- "You mean be with the one *animal spirit*?"

She doesn't reply. Her mission is over, I watch her dissolve and vanish into timelessness. She means I now know what fear to face and what to do. Face my dad issues so I can get a shot at a happier life.

-

The next morning pans out very much as Susana predicted; I cancel my appointments to spend the entire day on my own in a state of utter bliss which I never reconnected to since.

15. FIND THE ONE

My session with Susana and subsequent dream encounter with Betty left me bewildered to say the least, in a state of interrogation and of amazement. Whether it was just a dream or Betty's ghost visiting me isn't relevant. The revolutionary idea of letting love come into my life found anchorage in my mind and spread through my daily routines. I notice it in little things: I prepare breakfast with unusual care and have it without rushing. Much like during meals with the Bellagio family in Como. I stopped eating compulsively and adjusted my lifestyle with enhanced self-respect, self-care, which progressively branch out to my work, my social interactions, my inner circles. My rational mind still demands a more sophisticated justification than a dream to explain this new mindset which, to my surprise, now even includes wanting to build a family. It's as if Susana drew up my life path and Betty got me onboard the train.

I feel baffled enough by recent events to seek advice from Jenny, a therapist and good friend of mine. She is the straight talker type, who doesn't believe in sugar coating, even as a shrink. A few days later we sit down for coffee, I explain that a few therapy sessions might come handy, but first I need some down to earth advice from an expert I trust. I keep my canine chats to myself but share everything else; my recent liberating epiphanies, self-love being key to a less strenuous life -even a happy one- and that I plan on having a shot at it. I conclude describing the dream about Betty, clues and answers I got out of it, leading to a new life roadmap. Jenny thinks for a bit while sipping tea and asks:

- "Do you like dogs?"
  Shit, didn't see that one coming!
- "No. Not really. I mean, funny you should ask that, because, as it happens, I've been going through some sort of dog therapy, to sort of overcome my aversion towards them. Does that make sense?"
- "Not really, no. Please tell me more."

I go on to explain the childhood trauma with the German Shepherd, the St Bernard and how spending time with dogs opened up to the idea of dogs being good after all, which through projections and transference had led to thinking of myself as not being so bad either, which led to practicing self-love.

- "And how is that working out for you?"
- "What...? Self-love?"
- "Yeah. Self-love."
- "Well, I would say that it feels right, but it isn't constant. I mean, sometimes I over practice, which makes me self-absorbed and feels inauthentic. But overall, it's good."
- "Ok. Well, I can tell you two things; one is you don't need to see a shrink, you have clarity of mind. Your self-analysis is far from delusional and seems to have led you to a good place. Or at least, on a good path to a good place."
- "I am pleased to hear that; I thought you would send me to one of your colleagues."
- "Nah...You'd be wasting your time and money, not to mention that it could cost you the clarity you've got. At this stage, a shrink will probably bring more confusion and no solution. It is one of these *less is more* situations that you should let unfold. I think you are heading to good things... Congratulations."

Jenny seems confident and since she isn't the praising type, I welcome her promising diagnosis.

And I congratulate myself for not telling her that all this is the result of fictional conversations I've been having with dogs and that feel so real, that I have come to wonder if they might have been. Her diagnosis might be quite different then! Her output comes as a relief, although it doesn't provide any call to action or recommendation, nor any food for thought. Just go with the flow. That is when I realise that she hasn't shared yet the second thing that she mentioned. She is now on a work call. I sip tea as she finishes. Her call over, she apologises as I pour more tea into her cup.

- "So, Jenny, you said there were two things you had in mind. What was the other thing?"

Jenny is bringing her focus from the phone call back to our chat to string some thoughts and say:

- "Oh yes... I think you should get a dog."
- "Are you serious now?"
- "Serious as a heart attack."
- "What makes you think I should get a dog?"
- "You spend your free time with dogs and you're visited by a dog who once meant the world to you in your dreams, and hands you the keys to happiness on a telepathic silver platter. As a therapist, as a friend and a woman who trusts her intuition, I am telling you: get yourself a dog, Axel."

Here was an unambiguous advice that is more than I bargained for, and I don't know what do with. Me? Getting a fucking dog?

I suspect that considering building a family, *Betty*'s transcendental *visit* and Jenny's advice plotted for me to warm up to the challenge of owning a puppy.

A few weeks later, I stand in a pet store that I picked after a thorough online searching process. The store's quirky name "*Find the One*" caught my attention and prior to my coming, the more than accommodating store manager drew a shortlist of five puppies, through an email exchange which consisted in her handling my cluelessness about the whole decision-making process. I am now doing my best to formulate my expectations:

- "I am breed-agnostic but not keen on long hair and hygiene is key. Also, I need a smart dog."
- "That fits a few puppies I have in mind, including three suggested in the shortlist I provided. So why don't we start with those, we can always look at other options later."
- "That sounds great."

An hour later, I have my eyes on two puppies, none from the shortlist; a Yorkie that I hope, could be another *Poppy*, and a puddle who reminds me of Kiko, who reminds me of Kyoko, my first flame. Determined to get out of the store with a puppy but failing to make up my mind, I ask the saintly patient manager (who must be a Buddhist) for an opinion:

- "What do you say, besides wanting me dead?"
- "You're keen to get a dog, but look uninspired."
- "You must be exasperated, I am really sorry to keep you at it for so long," I say, eager to make sure she knows what I am putting her through.
- "You aren't the first nor the last. Don't worry about me. I don't sell dogs in here. I think of myself as a match maker, and I don't see much spark, I can't see *the love*, to tell you the truth."

There's the liberating comment that I had been unknowingly waiting for; am I feeling love? What's my emotional compass really saying?

- "Are you the owner of the store?" I ask.
- "I am, yes."
- "Well, in that case, I suppose that store is not called *Find the One* for no reason. Those puppies are lucky to have you, and I am not ready for any of them. At least not today. When I am, I won't buy my puppy from anywhere else but here. That is if you ever let me into you store again."
- "Lucky me!" she jokes, surely relieved to know that I am on my way out.
- "Before I go, please let me buy a store voucher for your time, I know *exactly* who to gift it to."

I do not. I just feel guilty and embarrassed to leave empty handed, after wasting this terrific woman's time and abusing her goodwill. And so I leave the store with a seventy-five-pound voucher in my pocket. I am about to reach my car and beep the door open, when I feel a brush rubbing the bottom of my trousers; it's a black and caramel coated puppy who seems lost. Its owner comes towards us to pick it up, apologising on behalf of her puppy wandering off. Meanwhile the puppy stares at me, and I instantly feel like cuddling it.

- "Please don't apologise" I assure the lady, "do you mind if I hold it for a second?"
- "Of course not, go ahead", she replies with a smile.
- "What breed is it?"
- "He is a Chiweenie."
- "I am sorry; a what?"
- "A Chiweenie. It is a mixed breed."

She explains that the pint-size hybrid I hold has the IQ of a *Chihuahua* and the spirited nature of a *Dachshund*. She goes on to highlight that it's also known as the *sausage dog*; the legendary long-bodied short-stubby legged, hound-type.
- "Chiweenies can be smooth-haired, wire-haired, or long-haired."

Hers is smooth haired, its shiny coat reminds me of Betty's, the look in its pearly eyes is almost a copycat of Poppy's hypnotic eyes..
- "He seems to like you," the lady notes.
- "I'm sure you say that to everyone. I'm not *Mister Dog*, but I have come a long way."

I feel comfortable to the point of pondering to let her in the know about my canine superpower, when a voice in my head (later identified as Betty's) urges me to shut up, which I do.
- "Well, my dog seems to be into *Mister not into Dogs*."
- "The feeling is mutual. Let me ask you something; did you buy your puppy here, at *Find the One*?" She looks perplexed. "I mean, the pet store behind us."
- "Of course, sorry" she replies spoiling me with a second elegant smile, "yes, I found him there. I'm actually heading in now."
- "Well, that's great." I reply, envious, wishing I had been as lucky to find a puppy like that, I would have snapped him on the spot.
- "Have you got a pet yourself then?" she asks, gap filling our improvised car park chat.
- "No. Not yet. In fact, I am looking for one. But it wasn't meant to be for today. Anyway, look, I won't be coming back here for a while and I've got a voucher from the store, why don't you use it for your adorable puppy..."

I hand the voucher to her, and press on, to ensure that she accepts.
- "your puppy made my day, please accept the voucher, giving it to you means more to me than its value can ever be worth to you."
- "Are you sure?"
- "Pawsitive" I try to joke.
- "Alright then. That is very kind of you, thank you. I shall use it now, getting him a new collar and name tag. That's lovely. Thanks again."
- "Great! What's his name?"
- "Axel."
- "I am sorry...what did you just say...?"
- "Axel. His name is Axel. I know, it's unusual."
- "The hell it is! That my name too!" I exclaim.
- "Really? What a coincidence! I think neither many dogs nor many people carry that name."

I hand the adorable *Axel* back to her. He's still staring at me and I can't take my eyes off him, despite his owner being to say the least, easy on the eye herself.
- "Indeed. What are the odds. Can I ask how you came to pick the name Axel for him?"
- "Oh no, that's a bit too strange to disclose to a stranger if I am honest," she replies.
- "Not even a stranger named as your dog?"
- "I usually don't reveal my quirks to strangers in a car park, or at least not without a drink. And for that one, probably the rest of the botte nearby."
- "If you are trying to get me to ask you out; done! I beg you to sound odd and quirky at will, if I have learnt one lesson in life, it is to not judge a book by its cover. Not that I am an avid reader... But that's beside the point...P*lease* do carry on."

She casually runs a hand through her hair, raise her eyes in what could be a decision-making routine and finally confesses:
- "Before him, I lost a dog, just over a year ago. I resisted getting another one, till few months ago, my dog came to visit me in a dream urging me to get another dog and name him *Axel*."
- "No fucking way! So sorry, forgive my French."
- "Well, you are French after all, aren't you? I detect a slight accent?"
- "How diplomatic of you, a slight accent; yes, I am. So, are you saying that...your deceased dog came to visit you in a dream...as a ghost?"
- "Right.... Told you it was weird... Is Mr. *Not Into Dogs* weirded out by Mrs. Dog Ghost yet?"

My silent compassionate look as sole reply to encourage her to carry on pays off:
- "The strangest thing is that my dog even gave me this store's name: *find the one at Find the One*. I found it two days after the dream."

She pauses, looks at me before suggesting:
- "Your car's open, good time to jump in and drive off from the car park mad woman, wouldn't you say?"
- "A good time to do precisely not that. You won't believe it, but I too was visited by a dog in a dream... Not mine but a dog I knew."
- "You're right, I don't believe you."
- "I promise you that it is true."
- "How strange! Good to know I'm not the only weirdo standing in this car park. Well, that's how I got him and got to name him Axel."
- "And what was his name?" I pursue.
- "I am sorry, I don't follow, whose name now?"
- "Your previous dog, whose *ghost* visited you in a dream. What was he called?"

- "Oh...I see. *Her* name. She was a female; Betty."

These last words feel like an earthquake, blasting a whole beneath my feet swallowing me into ground. an expression of panic crosses my face as I try to reason how I just came out of a pet store, bitter, empty handed, only to meet a delightful lady, owner of a puppy who I love at first sight, shares my name and whose name was suggested to the lady in a dream by *Betty*, her deceased dog who by the way, departed around the same time that the *Betty* who just visited me in my dream to tell me to *find the one*. It is at that point, that I did one of the smartest things I ever did in my life: I shut up my mind and let my heart take over. I describe Betty to the lady who burst into tears when she realises that I knew *her* Betty. Despite feeling magical this synchronicity, made no sense until she explained that she met *my* Betty during a holiday in France where her owners were actively looking for a new owner following a series of family complications. She fell in love with Betty at once and brought her back to England. I had not stayed in touch with the family in question, but I heard that they went through a synchronised torrent of health and financial hardship. Following this improbable revelation, I suggest coming with them into the store, a decision instantly approved by Axel the Chiweenie, who snorts happily and bounds forward. The reason I know this was my smartest moves ever is that this woman and I are now happily married and Axel, our Chiweenie has everything to do with it. The day we met, on our way out of the store, I offered to hug, we did. I then offered to keep in touch, we did. A week later, I asked her out, she accepted. Six months later she suggested moving together, I accepted. A year later

I proposed, she accepted and before we knew it, we were living a proper *fury tale*. Puppy Axel and grumpy Axel are both unashamedly happy. As for my life partner, the *"happy woof happy life"* mantra applies, I meant *"happy wife, happy life"*. Her name is Elizabeth. her colleagues call her Lizzy, but to her loved ones she is *Betty*. Axel the Chiweenie is my companion, my playmate, occasional footstool, and full-time therapist. And of course, we talk all the time. For our first conversation, he made sure to let me know that *he* had orchestrated my meeting Elizabeth in the car park and that he didn't sprint in my direction to bolt onto my leg by accident. When I asked why he did it, he said:

- "Dogs have dreams too. Before I saw you in the car park, a dog came to visit me in my sleep to say: *"next time Elizabeth takes you to the pet store, keep your eyes out for the lonely, confused man and run towards him. He's been waiting for you and Elizabeth for a long, long time."*
- "Was the dog short-haired, black, beautiful...
- "Emerald eyes, yes." completes Axel. "She also said you'd ask me that, once we found you."

Betty's ghost had united the three of us.

Canine *Axel* keeps on surprising me. I sometimes take him with me to the *"Find the One"* pet store when I need to go back there. To most it is a store. To me, it is the *"little did I know what the store had in store for me"* store. The store where I found the one...and the other one...the woofing one.

THE END

ABOUT THE AUTHOR

After two decades wandering in the corporate world, Axel became an improbable regression hypnotherapist and an even more improbable writer who strives to vulgarise opaque topics, occasionally with a dash of humour.

www.ingramcontent.com/pod-product-compliance
Lightning Source LLC
Chambersburg PA
CBHW031412040426
42444CB00005B/528